Good Housekeeping

EVERY HOME
SHOULD HAVE ONE

Good Housekeeping

EVERY HOME
SHOULD HAVE ONE

jan boxshall

EBURY PRESS
LONDON

First published in 1997

1 3 5 7 9 10 8 6 4 2

First published in the United Kingdom in 1997 by Ebury Press
Random House, 20 Vauxhall Bridge Road, London SW1V 2SA

Random House Australia (Pty) Limited
20 Alfred Street, Milsons Point, Sydney,
New South Wales 2061, Australia

Random House New Zealand Limited
187 Poland Road, Glenfield, Auckland 10, New Zealand

Random House South Africa (Pty) Limited
Endulini, 5a Jubilee Road, Parktown 2193, South Africa

Random House UK Limited Reg. No. 954009

A CIP catalogue record for this book is available from the British Library.

ISBN 0 09 185280 3

Text designed by Paul Wood
Cover designed by Design 23

Printed in Hong Kong by Midas Printing Limited

contents

acknowledgements

Thanks to Sharon Davies for her excellent research.

Thanks also to Emma Dally; to the staff of the National Magazine Company library for their help, particularly Susanna van Langenberg and Diane Courtney; to Suzanne Wilkinson of the Good Housekeeping Institute; and to former staff of the Institute Margaret Coombs, Gill Smedley and Jack Smith for their memories.

preface

Good Housekeeping magazine launched in the same year that the BBC was formed and the first telephone exchange opened in London, and thus three great means of communicating began. All have gone from strength to strength in 75 years.

Every month for three-quarters of a century the pages of *Good Housekeeping* have brought news, information, entertainment and advice on consumer choices to women. The journalists who compiled that first issue had the same aims as the current editorial team: to bring the best of everything to readers everywhere.

Our anniversary year brings the many domestic and social changes of past decades into focus. The magazine has always played an important role in the lives of women throughout modern history, and this book highlights the events, products and achievements that have had such a huge impact on the way we live today.

Good Housekeeping's heritage makes it unique in publishing history and its authority and content today assure its future for the years to come.

Pat Roberts Cairns, Editor-in-Chief, *Good Housekeeping*

INTRODUCTION

the way it was

IN THE SEVENTY-FIVE YEARS SINCE THE FIRST issue of *Good Housekeeping* was published, with the hopeful claim that 'there should be no drudgery in the home', home life in Britain has been transformed. Decades of amazing technological development, combined with increasing affluence and the emancipation of women, have irrevocably changed the way we live. Within just two generations, machines have enabled people to live more comfortably with less effort; standards of hygiene have risen greatly; radio, television and video have made the home a self-sufficient entertainment centre; while telephones, cars and now home computers have widened the horizons of family life. To appreciate how dramatic the changes have been, it is necessary to look at the way in which homes were arranged at the start of the century.

In the decades preceding 1922, when *Good Housekeeping* was launched, progress in domestic life had taken place at a relative snail's pace. The nineteenth century, in the wake of the Industrial Revolution, saw the important development of gas and electricity supplies, although apart from gas lighting, these two new sources

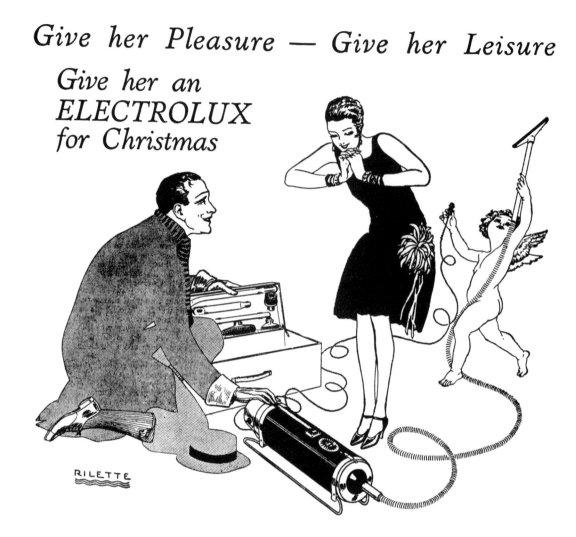

Give her Pleasure — Give her Leisure

Give her an
ELECTROLUX
for Christmas

RILETTE

The wonderful Cleaner that every woman covets!

The moment a woman with a house to look after sees the Electrolux suction cleaner at work, she longs to possess it. Such easy, effortless, efficient cleaning of every nook and corner! Dust banished—germs destroyed—the very air of the room sweetened and purified in a few minutes. Hours of labour saved. Dust cleared from under the heaviest furniture without stooping, carpets thoroughly cleaned without being taken up.

There is no cleaner like Electrolux—none so powerful, nor yet so handy and compact. Electrolux is the very last word in up-to-date domestic efficiency.

Give her an Electrolux this Christmas—it means a New Year of leisure and freedom—and not only *one* New Year but a lifetime of them!

The NEW
ELECTROLUX
THE *CLEANER* CLEANER

ELECTROLUX, LIMITED, 155, Regent St., London, W.1.   Works: Luton.
Showrooms throughout the Country.
Makers also of Electrolux Motorless Refrigerators and Water Softeners.

of power had yet to make a major impact on home life. The amount of gadgetry had begun to increase, with inventions such as the spirit iron and the hand-operated carpet sweeper taking some of the pain out of housework, but they were still hard work to use. In the early twentieth century, before the First World War brought social and technological revolution in its wake, housework was hard work.

Labour-Intensive Living

The average middle-class home before the war was usually a substantial house, often a three- or four-storey Victorian or Edwardian terrace which was labour-intensive to run. Decorations were still heavily influenced by Victorian style – heavy draperies, picture rails, ornately carved furniture and an abundance of dust-trapping ornaments and pictures made heavy work of cleaning. Lighting was often by gas (although electric light was slowly being introduced) which created dirty fumes, and most rooms were heated by open fires, which needed daily sweeping, cleaning and setting. In spite of the lack of some comforts we take for granted today, standards in the home were at levels most women now would find ridiculous – cleaning and dusting were daily tasks; doorsteps were polished and brass kept sparkling; linen starched – and spring-cleaning was planned like a military campaign. All this was done without the aid of modern detergents: Fuller's earth powder, emery paper, black lead and soap flakes were some of the maid's weapons in the war against dirt.

It was in the kitchen that the difference from today's houses was most striking. The kitchen, laundry and larder were usually in the basement, so were often gloomy places. Although gas cookers had been available since 1890, they were slow to catch on in the early twentieth century, largely because inadequate gas supplies made them unreliable, but also because there were quite justified fears of explosion. Cooking was usually done on a coal-fired cast-iron range which required daily cleaning, frequent black-leading and polishing. Crockery was often displayed on open shelves, so needed frequent cleaning; floors were stone or slate; worktops were wood and needed daily scrubbing. Washing was a mammoth task, usually

ALSO ON DISPLAY AT

Available from leading department stores and ma

UR LOCAL SHOWROOM.

trical retailers. For your nearest stockist telephone 081 573 1199 or for a brochure only 081 561 9998.

BOSCH

Excellence comes as standard

taking a couple of days: clothes and bedding were soaked, washed and rinsed in a giant boiler or copper, whites were 'blued', and everything was wrung by hand and starched before ironing (often still with an iron heated on the range). Some hand-operated washing machines were available, usually wooden drums in which clothes were agitated by a wooden handle, but these were expensive and still used a lot of elbow grease. Carpets had to be swept or beaten clean, though vacuum cleaners were on their way – in the early twentieth century giant vacuums were towed around on carts and parked outside houses while their suction tubes were passed in through doors and windows. Keeping food fresh was a problem, but basement larders kept food reasonably cool, and some homes had ice boxes which were literally that, insulated boxes cooled by ice, delivered by the ice man.

Leave it to the Servants

Maintaining reasonable standards of cleanliness and warmth took considerable time and effort – there were no shortcuts but, in an era when servants were in plentiful supply, running such a labour-intensive household wasn't a problem. It was common for middle-class homes to employ a live-in maid to do the heavy housework, a laundress and possibly a cook, not to mention a nanny or nurse to shoulder the burden of childcare, leaving the lady of the house to do a little light dusting and sewing and to organise her staff and menus. Most supplies were delivered to the door by the grocer, fishmonger, butcher and dairy; even dressmakers would provide a home service. The well-to-do housewife before the First World War didn't often need to get her hands dirty, and was free to devote herself to good works, tea parties and entertaining on a grand scale. Family life revolved around mealtimes, perhaps piano playing or (in progressive households) listening to the gramophone, and church on Sundays.

This relative luxury was, of course, limited to the middle and upper classes. For the working-class woman, who had no help whatsoever and usually lived in far more basic, cramped conditions without running hot water or a bathroom, keeping home and hearth together was exhausting, and the standard of living taken for granted in middle-class homes was undreamed-of luxury. One of the greatest benefits of technology in the twentieth century must be that it has raised the general standard of living, cutting down many of the huge differences between women in their ways of life.

This book tells the story of the changing face of housework and home life, from the days of mangles and black-leading to microwaves and home computers, as recorded in the pages of *Good Housekeeping* for three-quarters of a century.

the 1920s:

DRUDGERY FLIES OUT AT THE WINDOW

IN MARCH 1922, WHEN *GOOD HOUSEKEEPING* was launched promising to 'meet the needs of the homekeeping woman of today', the time was ripe for a magazine of its kind. The sweeping social changes brought about by the First World War meant that life had changed irrevocably for the middle-class housewife, and she needed help to meet the challenge.

The Servant Problem

The housewife's problem was that she simply couldn't find any domestic staff to help her run her cumbersome home. The young working-class girls who had previously been reasonably happy to work a 16-hour day for a pittance were liberated by the war. Called upon to take the place of men in factories, shops and offices, they found they could earn more in a week than they had in a month in service, and also discovered the pleasure of being treated as equals, not servants. It was hardly surprising that they showed little enthusiasm for returning to service – leaving middle-class women to run their homes single-handed, or at best with the help of a 'daily'. The change is reflected in *Good Housekeeping's* advertising during

The Reason For
GOOD HOUSEKEEPING

*" Neither do men light a candle, and put it
under a bushel, but on a candlestick ; and it
giveth light unto all that are in the house "*

ANY keen observer of the times cannot have failed to notice that we are on the threshold of a great feminine awakening. Apathy and levity are alike giving place to a wholesome and intelligent interest in the affairs of life, and above all in the home. We believe that the time is ripe for a great new magazine which shall worthily meet the needs of the homekeeping woman of to-day.

There should be no drudgery in the house. There must be time to think, to read, to enjoy life, to be young with the growing generation, to have time for their pleasures, to have leisure for one's own—to hold one's youth as long as possible, to have beauty around us—line and colour in dress, form and colour in our surroundings; to have good food without monotony, and good service without jangled tempers.

It will be the aim of GOOD HOUSEKEEPING to meet these needs and to forestall them. The daily life of women—what concerns them and interests them most profoundly and most intimately, what they talk about, think about, and wish to read about in their favourite magazine —will be the first concern of GOOD HOUSEKEEPING. The burning questions of the day will be reflected each month in articles by women in the public eye, known for their sound grasp of their subject—by women who can lead women, and who are fearless, frank, and outspoken. All sides and phases of women's interest—art, music, and the drama, and the social side of life—will find a place on our platform, and both sides of every open question will be given a hearing, though partisan politics and parties will be rigorously excluded. Women writers, whose words are waited for and whose views are valued by other women all over the kingdom, will be among our honoured contributors.

The house-proud woman in these days of servant shortage does not always know the best ways to lessen her own burdens. Household management will be a feature of GOOD HOUSEKEEPING, and every new invention that is practical and economical in use will be brought to her notice after careful examination month by month. The time spent on housework can be enormously reduced in every home, without any loss to its comfort, and often with a great increase to its well-being and its air of personal care and attention.

Fashions will be an important feature of GOOD HOUSEKEEPING. They will be in two sections—French and English. A very exclusive and complete service of French fashions, such as has not been hitherto supplied to any English magazine, will be sent over by our representatives in Paris, where we have an office and staff who will keep in closest touch with all the great French houses and contribute sketches that will anticipate every change in line. They will supply designs that we venture to think will be found of extraordinary value to those whose business it is to study fashion as well as to those whose pleasure it is to follow it. Our French fashion service will be something quite unique in the history of Women's papers. English fashions will be seen reflected in sketches from the great London houses. They will also be an important feature. English fashions have steadily improved in taste and design, and it will be the pleasant duty of GOOD HOUSEKEEPING to show how very good they are—and to help those of our readers who are out of reach of the London shops to buy the very best that is being shown in them. There will be a shopping service in connection with the sketches from the London shops, and this service will be available to all our readers.

Home cookery is nearly always good, but the family menu is sometimes a little monotonous because the housekeeper has no time to test new dishes and has a certain suspicion of the *untested* recipe. Well, in the offices of GOOD HOUSEKEEPING, a modern and properly equipped kitchen has been installed, and there every recipe before being printed will be tested, and only those recipes which have passed the test of a widely known practical cookery expert, skilled in the knowledge of what a family welcomes, will be given. These dishes, old and new, will be closely described, and there will be nothing casual about their choice or their explanations. They will be well worth keeping in the note-book that is always found on the good housekeeper's kitchen shelf.

House decoration changes with other fashions, and the house-proud woman likes to know what is being done in big and little houses —how cretonnes are coloured and patterned for country house and town house, how furniture is being made for bedroom and living-room, what periods are influencing cabinet-making and the little accessories of the house from toilet mirror to footstool. These things, too, will be described month by month in GOOD HOUSEKEEPING, so that the house itself shall always have that up-to-date look that other women recognise. For though women are supposed to dress themselves to please their men-folk, they deck their houses most often for each other.

Fiction is one of the pleasures of most women's leisure, and good fiction only—wholesome and suited to a magazine that will find its way into thousands of homes and that will be read, we hope, with equal pleasure by all the members of the household—will be given, and will be from the pens of our greatest and best-known novelists.

The good housekeeper is "the keystone of the arch" and "the pillar of the house." She is worthy of a great magazine, and it will be our aim to make GOOD HOUSEKEEPING worthy of her.

The introduction to the first ever issue of Good Housekeeping

the roaring twenties

1922	*Good Housekeeping* magazine was launched
	The first telephone exchange in London opened
	The British Broadcasting Company was formed, making regular radio broadcasts
	The first electric powered dishwasher in Britain was developed
1923	The Swan kettle was invented, the first to have a separate element
	The first electric fridge was sold in the UK
1924	The Ministry of Health banned preservatives in cream, butter, margarine and other foodstuffs
	Pyrex glassware was introduced in Britain.
1926	The founding of the Central Electricity Board and the establishment of the National Grid took place
	The General Strike
	The first all-electric gramophone was developed
1928	The Equal Franchise Act gave the vote to all women over 21
	The first television set went on sale in US
	The first 'talkie' was shown in a UK cinema.
1929	The Wall Street Crash triggered a worldwide depression
	The first public telephone boxes were installed
	The Aga was invented by Swede Gustav Dalen
	A small electric oven, the Baby Belling, appeared on the market

the 1920s: at the beginning of the decade many adverts still featured servants doing heavy housework; but by 1929 the mop or vacuum was firmly in the hands of the mistress of the house.

'The servant problem', as it was called, left women fending for themselves and, as *Good Housekeeping* tactfully observed, 'The house-proud woman in these days of servant shortage does not always know the best ways to lessen her own burdens.' The magazine, already a success in America where women had been servantless for a lot longer, stepped into the breach, filling a gap in the women's magazine market by advising women on servantless household management, recommending recipes, and guiding readers through the maze of domestic gadgetry which was springing up to take the place of servants' hands – as well as providing the more traditional diet of fashion, fiction and features.

The New Servants

Fortunately for the bereft housewife, the social changes of the 1920s went hand in hand with a technological revolution, and the decline in human servants was accompanied by the rise of two far more biddable household resources – gas and, more importantly, electricity. In the space of just one decade, speeded up by the housewife's hunger for labour-saving devices, they were harnessed for household tasks from cooking and washing to sweeping the floor and keeping food fresh.

Gas was already piped into many homes for gas lighting, but its potential for cooking and heating had been barely exploited before the 1920s. Electricity, meanwhile, although hugely popular in America, had been slower to catch on in Britain, mainly due to problems with the lack of a proper structure for supply, plus a general suspicion of this 'trained lightning' (shocks were quite common from early appliances). But the war had prompted developments in gas and electricity supply, and now the population at large could benefit.

The main task for gas and electricity suppliers in the 1920s was to convince the housewife of the benefits of switching from tried and trusted coal and oil to the new fuels. Adverts from the Commercial Gas Association appear in *Good Housekeeping* throughout the 1920s, with Mr

Below and overleaf: The British Commercial Gas Association used the pages of Good Housekeeping *to convince housewives of the benefits of gas.*

The kitchen in the all-gas house showing gas cooker with plate rack above, modern gas fire and gas-heater circulator. In the adjoining scullery are fixed a gas fire, incinerator, a gas copper, and an internally heated gas iron.

No Small Achievement

TO warm a house comfortably, light it pleasantly, ensure cooking that is dependable, and hot water in plenty— all without extravagance—is no small achievement. Yet all this can be done with perfect ease by using gas

*Write for Gas Economy Leaflet No. 1
.. on the " All-Gas House " to . .*

THE BRITISH COMMERCIAL GAS ASSOCIATION

30 GROSVENOR   GARDENS, S.W.1

"That's good-bye to unnecessary drudgery

Mr. G. A. SERVICE
on the Saving of Labour.

" . . . good-bye to all the work and trouble of fire-making, cleaning grates, and removing ashes. The gas fire, madam, can be lighted in a second and it starts, stays, and finishes clean.
" You'll find it's the same with all gas appliances. In fact, madam, whenever *heat* is needed—whether for warming rooms, cooking food, heating water, or burning refuse — gas is the ideal fuel for the ideal home."

* * *

The B.C.G.A., representing the British Gas Industry, is at the service of the public, without charge, for advice and help on any subject, large or small, connected with the economical and efficient use of gas in the home.
Mr. G. A. Service will welcome enquiries sent to him at the address below.

GAS
for Homes of To-day

THE BRITISH COMMERCIAL GAS ASSOCIATION, 28 GROSVENOR GARDENS, LONDON, S.W. 1.

Before replying to advertisements refer to page 106. 107

G A Service boasting to his female customer after installing her new gas fire, 'That's goodbye to unnecessary drudgery.' The rival Electrical Development Association, meanwhile, was set up to persuade women to embrace 'the invisible servant', and in 1924 the Electrical Association for Women was founded (led by a rare female engineer) to act as a pressure group to convince women of its cleanliness and efficiency. *Good Housekeeping* played its part in promoting electricity, claiming somewhat optimistically in a 1922 feature on time-saving devices that 'when electricity comes in at the door, drudgery flies out at the window'.

Gas rapidly won the battle as the preferred fuel for cooking and heating, but it was electricity that truly transformed the home. The establishment of the National Grid in 1926 improved distribution, while the invention of the small motor meant that electricity could be harnessed to replace hand power in appliances such as sewing and washing machines. *Good Housekeeping* described the motor as 'the up-to-date substitute for elbow grease' and 'the most promising means of escape from the hard labour of domestic life'.

Manufacturers of both gas and electrical appliances were quick to realise the potential of the new servantless class, and technological development raced ahead on an unprecedented scale, with new gadgets flooding the market, all making extravagant advertising claims. The phrase 'labour saving' had barely been heard before the 1920s – when there was no shortage of hands it wasn't an issue –

but in this decade it became a mantra. Appliances were the new servants: Hoover made direct appeals to 'the maidless mistress', while makers of the Apex suction cleaner claimed, 'The Apex is as good as a whole staff of well-trained servants.' A favourite phrase of the time, imported originally from America, was: 'Every home should have one.'

The Joy of Housework

As well as selling their products, manufacturers were selling the image of housework, and as a result the 1920s saw a dramatic change in the way the housewife was perceived. Previously, heavy domestic work was regarded as drudgery best left to servants, something the decent woman wouldn't sully her hands with, but now advertisements and editorial features alike made a virtue out of necessity and raised the status of housework. Articles extolled the pleasures of keeping a clean, well-organised home and, if adverts were to be believed, keeping a clean house was the pinnacle of female achievement. In 1922, Viscountess Gladstone described the model housewife as someone 'probably born and not made', while in 1928, in an article entitled 'Are you a good housekeeper?', Lady Violet Bonham Carter said, 'The mechanism of a house well kept should be silent and absolutely invisible. Really good housekeeping is neither seen nor heard.'

As if to make housework more palatable – surely no one was fooled? – housekeeping was described as a science, not a chore. *Good Housekeeping* encouraged women to take a pride in 'the business of housekeeping'. An entire department was dedicated to 'Household engineering and housecraft', and monthly features advised women on running a home, choosing appliances and organising their time. In 1925, it advised women to 'organise your work as a man organises his business, and modernise your methods and equipment'. With the magazine's help, 'domestic work ceases to be drudgery and becomes a fascinating science'. The kitchen was given new status as 'The working centre of the house, the laboratory in which the family meals are prepared.'

HOME MANAGEMENT

Conducted by *Mary Penfold*

First-Class Diploma, National Training School of Cookery and Domestic Subjects, and Examiner in Domestic Subjects

Save your Time!

DO you know that you are entitled to a certain amount of time all your own, and that it is most necessary you should have it to improve your mind and increase your poise? You can have this time which is due to you only by casting aside old-fashioned methods of housekeeping and by adopting newer ones. Such methods are described in the pages of this department. All our experimenting and research are for the purpose of helping you, therefore you can use each suggestion with confidence. When needing information, write, enclosing a stamped and addressed envelope, to the Department of Home Management, "GOOD HOUSEKEEPING," 1 Amen Corner, London, E.C.4

Time-Savers and Labour-Savers

By *Adam Gowans Whyte, B.Sc., A.I.E.E.*

MANY a housewife, worn out by the incompetence of maids or by the frequent process of "doing without," must have consoled herself with visions of the day when all the household machinery will run itself at the touch of a button. Every now and then we read a description of some sort of Arabian Nights home where tables already laid for dinner rise through the floor, and where all the domestic routine, from the early-morning cup of tea to the final nightcap, is fulfilled by automatic and unseen contrivances.

All such homes are, as the practical housewife knows in her heart, dreams of beautiful nonsense. So long as there are meals to be cooked and served, rooms to keep clean, or fabrics and dishes to be washed, so long will the human hand be needed to do something more than touch a button. And even if the automatic home were possible, it would need to be a totally new one, specially constructed in every detail. The problem for most of us is to make the best of ordinary houses, designed on the assumption that servants would never be a disappearing or degenerate species.

Put in a sentence, the problem is to save time and labour in carrying out everyday duties in the home. With a true instinct we look to electricity for special help. It is not for nothing that the utopian push-button homes are "all electric"; the buttons are invariably electric buttons. The peculiarity of electricity is that it tends to reduce a long process of work and preparation to the simple turning of a switch.

We see this clearly—although we do not always realise its meaning—in the case of electric light. The housewives of old had to see to the cleaning, filling, trimming, and lighting of many lamps. To-day they are relieved of that long and laborious nuisance. All the work required to

When electricity comes in at the door drudgery flies out at the window, and breakfast, incidentally, becomes the pleasantest meal of the day

Good Housekeeping's *department of* **home** *management,* *later the* **Institute,** *encouraged* *women to take* *a business-like* *approach to* **housework.**

oduce light is done at
e electricity station ;
d the labour imposed
 the user of light is
luced to the negligible
le of touching a
itch.
Thus electric light in
e home is a material
ver of labour. Its
treme convenience
ans, however, some-
ng more than a re-
ction of work. It is
 source of economy.
hen it is so simple
d easy a matter to
itch a light off, there
 no temptation to
ste light by leaving
mps burning un-
cessarily. This point
 of great interest in
nnection with other
es of electricity in
e home—those uses
and which the sus-
cion of being expen-
e still hangs.
When those " other
es " are mentioned,
st people think
st of electric fires
d electric cooking
ages. In a practical
se they are opening
e domestic electrical
ok at the last chapters
tead of at the first.
hile electric heating
d cooking, properly
ed, bring many benefits—as we shall
ow later—they involve a material
tlay on special wiring and also on
paratus. Not many housewives who
 familiar with electric light alone
ll be ready to incur this expense right
ay. But if they have gained some
tual experience of " other uses " of a
re moderate character, they will feel
nfident that the change to electric
oking and heating will be well worth
ile.
In this first article, therefore, we shall
scribe only those domestic applica-
ns of electricity which can be made
 small cost by anyone who has electric
ht in the house. These applications
e more varied than people suppose ;
d they all tend to the saving of labour.
At once the most popular and most
aracteristic of these " other uses " is
orded by the electric iron. When the
l-fashioned black iron is employed,
ne is wasted in carrying irons back-
rds and forwards to and
m the place where they
e heated. Time is wasted
testing whether the iron
 hot enough ; heat is
sted because it pours out
 a black article like water
rough a sieve ; and labour
 wasted because, as the
n gets rapidly cooler, it
s to be banged down and
essed hard to make it do
 work.
Contrast this with the
e of the electric iron, with
 electric heating element
ncealed inside a bright
ckel-plated base which al-
ays remains clean. Within

Ironing ceases to be a task and becomes a pleasure when an
electric iron is used

a minute of switching on, the iron is hot
enough for use ; and thereafter the
ironing can proceed without interrup-
tion. It does its work so easily that all
but the heaviest fabrics can be ironed
while the ironer remains seated. Long
before a batch of ironing is completed
the current can be switched off and
the remainder—preferably light articles
such as handkerchiefs—finished with
the heat retained in the bright iron.
Modern electric irons are fitted with a
support on which they can be conveniently rested during the intervals of
work ; and a switch is often fitted in the
connector to the iron so as to give the
easiest possible control of the current.
This contrast has been drawn in
some detail because it illustrates the

chief claims made for
domestic electric appli-
ances : their readiness
for immediate service,
their cleanliness, the
ease of control, and
the manner in which
they save time and
labour. It is no ex-
aggeration to say that
the electric iron trans-
forms a task into a
p l e a s u r e . Many a
woman now reserves for
treatment with her own
electric iron the dainty
fabrics which were pre-
viously scorched or
soiled by the old black
iron in the hands of a
destructive maid.
Next to the electric
iron, the electric kettle
probably makes the
strongest appeal. To
be able to boil up two
or three pints of water
on the table or in a
bedroom without any
preparations save the
filling of the kettle and
the switching on of the
current is a real boon.
The housewife who likes
to make her own tea
will find that the elec-
tric kettle makes every-
thing as simple and easy
as possible. Related
to the electric kettle
there is quite a series
of electric table or bedroom appliances,
such as hot-water jugs, shaving-water
heaters, milk warmers, egg boilers, and
chafing-dishes. Most welcome of all,
however, to many fastidious people is
the electric coffee percolator. It re-
duces the process of making coffee to
the lowest terms of trouble and raises
it to the highest in perfection. Cold
water is placed in the base of the percolator and coffee in the sieve-like upper
part ; then the current is switched on,
and after a definite interval, depending
on the quantity of water, the coffee is
ready.
Both the electric kettle (or teapot)
and percolator can be used, as already
hinted, on the table—a feature which
is in itself a great convenience. The
same advantage is enjoyed by the electric toaster and the electric grill. In
the toaster a slice of bread is placed
on each side of an upright electric
heating element and reversed as soon
as necessary. The latest
forms of electric toaster
have a simple automatic
arrangement which enables
one to reverse the bread
without touching it. Crisp
golden-brown toast is the
invariable result. The electric grill has a radiant heating element under a re-
flector, and its even, clean
heat will grill bacon, kid-
neys, tomatoes, and so on
in a way which cannot be
excelled.
With such electric appli-
ances, it should be noted,
a complete breakfast can

An electric iron heats in one minute, keeps hot, and is always
perfectly clean

Come out of the kitchen!

and leave all the cooking to the **Parkinson** "NEW SUBURBIA" Gas Cooker.

Cooking requires no close attention because of the automatic oven heat control. In addition, it has the unique feature of having two flues and one burner in the oven itself. The top flue allows condensation moisture to escape, then closes automatically, after which the heat circulates all round the oven. Thus you get much more heat from much less gas consumption.

Ask for a demonstration at your local Gas Showrooms, but make sure you are shown the **Parkinson** "NEW SUBURBIA" Gas Cooker.

Descriptive Booklet "G" gladly sent upon request.

IT DOES ALL THE COOKING WHILE YOU SHOP OR PLAY

Parkinson and Electrolux wooed women with promises of increased leisure time, while Hoover played on guilt feelings.

THE PARKINSON 'NEW SUBURBIA' GAS COOKER

THE PARKINSON STOVE CO., LTD., Stechford, **BIRMINGHAM**
London Showrooms: 8 & 10 Grosvenor Gardens, S.W.1. *And at* Glasgow, Manchester, Belfast, Dublin

In 1924 the Good Housekeeping Institute was founded to test recipes, and also to 'submit all domestic appliances to exhaustive tests and bring those approved to the notice of all housewives'. And there was certainly no shortage of goods to be tested.

Perhaps the first major change of the 1920s was the increasing use of the gas cooker to replace the old cast-iron stove. Earlier versions had still been made in cast iron, but a new generation of part-enamelled cookers such as the Parkinson Suburbia, often featuring the 'Regulo'

thermostat invented in 1923 to control heat, offered a cleaner, more efficient way of cooking – and brought an end to the ritual of black-leading. A fully enamelled version appeared in 1927. Some electric cookers also came on to the market in the 1920s, but they didn't seriously compete with gas until thermostatic control was introduced in the 1930s. In 1929 came a new invention from Sweden which has proved to be one of the most enduringly popular kitchen appliances – the Aga.

If Only For Your Children's Sake

Motor Mania

Electricity made a major impact in the smaller appliances powered by motor. The vacuum cleaner was the most instantly successful of these. It was invented by James Spangler in 1908 using his wife's pillowcase as a dustbag, and, had he not sold his patent to Hoover, millions of homes worldwide would presumably Spangle their carpets today. The Hoover promised to 'make house cleaning easy', and it certainly was a huge improvement on carpet beating. A host of other brands followed, and in 1927,

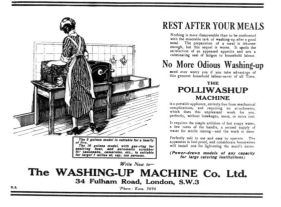

Electrolux boasted, 'Give her pleasure – give her leisure. Give her an Electrolux for Christmas.'

The motor also powered washing machines. At first these were wooden tubs in a metal shell with a motor replacing elbow grease, but towards the end of the decade metal tubs with internal 'agitators' were introduced. Similar in design were early dishwashers, such as the hand-operated Polliwashup (above), which wooed women with the promise 'No more odious washing-up', or the primitive electric dishwasher which had to be filled with boiling water. These early models were expensive, inefficient, and didn't sell in significant numbers.

Another major development of the early 1920s was the refrigerator – although early models were noisy, big and expensive. Gas and electricity competed for dominance here, but the cleanliness of the electric fridge won out. After 1924, when the use of certain preservatives in fresh food was banned, fridge adverts played on the housewife's most vulnerable spot, guilt, by giving dire warnings about the dangers of contaminated food. This increased sales, but by 1931 only around 200,000 homes had fridges.

These larger appliances were initially very expensive to buy, especially as many were imported from America, and it was common for women to hire cookers, washing machines and fridges throughout the 1920s.

Smaller electrical appliances were

THE MONTH'S SELECTED APPLIANCE

Each month a page will be devoted to an account of a household appliance of special interest and having a high standard of efficiency

The dryer holds about 7 lb. of clothes and these are automatically freed from excess moisture in about 3 minutes

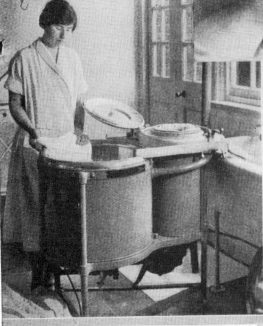

Both the washer and the dryer can be operated at the same time

An Electric Washing Machine

now being tested at the Institute

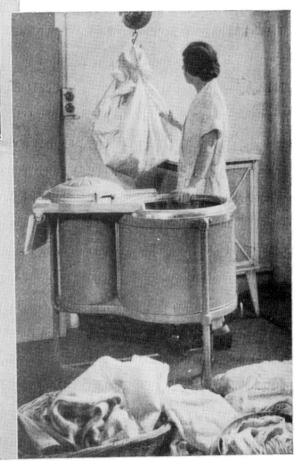

At the start of a test on a washing machine each load of clothes is weighed

THE electric washer and dryer illustrated on this page is one of the latest machines tested at the Institute, where it has been used for washing household linen and cotton, silk and woollen garments. In a large household, where all laundrywork is undertaken at home, the time and labour saved with a machine such as this is almost incalculable.

The washing machine itself is one of the latest type, with central agitator revolving first in one direction and then in the other, but it is the dryer and convenient automatic means of emptying which make this machine a particularly desirable acquisition. The dryer is of the centrifugal type, and is, in fact, a smaller model of the hydro-extractor in use in up-to-date laundries. It has many advantages over a wringer, for a complete load of washing can be automatically freed from moisture merely by filling up the cylindrical container and turning on the current. Drying is very thorough, and although the amount of water extracted depends to a large extent on the length of time the dryer is operated, clothes are almost as dry in 3 minutes as when passed twice through the average hand or electrically driven rubber wringer, and if they are allowed to remain longer in the dryer, still more moisture is extracted.

Other advantages that

Left: **Notice the maid in this early 1920s advertisement for refrigerators**

Above: **Good Housekeeping** *rigorously tested new appliances such as this bulky washing machine.*

more affordable, and quickly became popular. The Swan electric kettle, the first kettle to feature a separate water-heating element, was invented in 1923; electric irons replaced black irons (though at first they had no thermostatic control) and prompted *Good Housekeeping* to claim: 'it is no exaggeration to say that the electric iron transforms a task into a pleasure'. The electric toaster was invented, the electric sewing machine had a motor to replace arm or foot power, and electric mixers, which were sometimes called mechanical kitchenmaids, took some of the work out of beating, mixing and mincing. These small appliances were often plugged into light fittings – a safety nightmare by today's standards.

'It is no exaggeration to say that the electric iron transforms a task into a pleasure.'

Thanks to these developments, the appearance of the kitchen began to change: heavy cast-iron ranges were replaced by light enamelled stoves; electric light replaced dirty gas lighting; refrigerators replaced the ice box. New aluminium pans were lighter and much easier to clean than the old cast-iron pots, and Pyrex clear glass utensils, introduced in Britain in 1924, were a revelation. Bakelite was the first plastic to make an impact in the home: it was popular for light switches and doorknobs, and later for telephones and radios. Enclosed kitchen cabinets replaced the more typical dressers, which meant that pots and crockery stayed cleaner, and the purpose-built kitchen cabinet became an object of desire. This was one giant cupboard with a pull-out table designed so that everything needed for cooking – crockery, cutlery, groceries – was in one place. These cabinets became more and more complicated, with cookbook holders, flour and sugar dispensers and built-in storage jars. *Good Housekeeping* said of the kitchen cabinet, 'Perhaps there is no one piece of furniture that can do more to economise space and reduce the drudgery of kitchen work.'

If Mr Spangler hadn't sold his suction machine patent to Hoover, would we spangle our carpets today?

The 1920s also saw the development of more effective detergents, including famous names such as Harpic (invented by British scientist Harry Pickup using the white waste powder from munitions factories, with a formulation which remained unchanged until the 1960s), and Persil, whose advert showed a woman going to the cinema, with the slogan 'time for the pictures on washday'.

It wasn't just the kitchen that was changing: housing and home life were also evolving. The substantial houses previously favoured by the middle-classes were hard to manage without servants and the trend was to decamp to smaller, easy-to-run homes in the new suburbs, leaving the large terraces to be split into flats. Four million new houses were built between the wars, mainly in the south-east in suburbs and 'planned' towns such as Welwyn Garden City, with wide streets and public parks. The new houses were detached or semi-detached, with three or four bedrooms, built-in bathrooms, kitchens on the ground floor, and were usually wired for electricity. There were no longer fireplaces in every room, or dust-collecting picture rails, and all in all the new houses were far easier for women to keep clean single-handed. The smallness of the new houses meant that

New detergents made washday easier – although perhaps not this easy

Occupying, with a well-planned garden, half **an acre** of ground, the servantless house is as ornamental as it is practical

The *Servantless* House

Solving the Problem of Costly Living

By DORA J. MOORE

CONVENTION dictates a certain standard of living for the professional and upper middle-class, be the individual family rich or poor; and since the days when dividends dwindled and prices soared, retrenchment has become a necessity in many a post-war household.

My own particular ménage was no exception to the rule. Life soon resolved itself into a sordid struggle to make two ends meet. It was during a caravan holiday that first the idea of defying convention and revolutionising our whole mode of living occurred to us. After a few peaceful days of the simple life, one begins to realise how unnecessarily encumbered is domestic life for the average housewife.

Admitted that caravan life might not be practicable for family life, I conceived the feasibility of enlarging on the idea and building a home that would have all the advantages of a caravan—except mobility!—and none of the disadvantages of an ordinary house. A compact little place, with one big room over the ground floor wherein children might play, out of sight and out of sound. A home built and equipped to reduce housework to a minimum—so that servants might be entirely dispensed with.

It did not take us long to put the scheme into action. An

A CARAVAN holiday was the inspiration of the enviable house described in this article, which many women will recognise as the cottage of their dreams come true. Planned very cleverly it fully lives up to its name, and few people, given the opportunity, would refuse to undertake its management unaided. The cost of its construction at the present time is about £1,500.

architect friend was commissioned to professionalise our own rough plans and sketches, and soon the cottage of our dreams was materialising on half an acre of ground on the river-side.

The venture held for us all the thrill of pre-married days, with this difference: after ten years of housekeeping, we now knew exactly what we required of our roof-tree—and the practical way to set out to get it.

Nearly all our old, cumbersome furniture was disposed of at a sale. The proceeds more than paid the expense of installing, throughout the entire cottage, fitments to our own design, to suit our personal requirements. Thus we utilised every inch of space to advantage and reduced housework, by abolishing the dust-traps that lurk below and above ordinary articles of furniture.

My long-suffering architect friend must have found us exacting clients; for we determined the cottage should be as picturesque as practical—combining all modern conveniences with the minimum of housework. Luckily, he is a man of resource as well as an artist, and rose to the occasion.

The living-room of the cottage is 16 feet by 16 feet 6 inches, and is literally panelled with oak book-cases. These, with their leaded lights, provide a com-

Articles such as this one in June 1923 helped the middle classes cope with their new, servantless living conditions

able home for our treasures, pleasing to the eye, *and* ·proof.

·he window-seat recess is long enough to be used as a ·ge couch, and under it are fitted handy cupboards. ·ms and other woodwork in this room are stained ·vn. A floor of polished oak is partly covered with ·an rugs. The restful, dominant colour throughout the ·n is soft-toned green. It was a debatable point whether ·sitting-room should or should not have a fireplace, for ·gh ample provision had been made for heating it ·uately by radiators, there is cheeriness about an open ·that most English folk find indispensable on dull days.

·ly architect produced such a fascinating sketch for a ·burning hearth that I succumbed to the idea; the more ·ly as he suggested that the space under-stairs should ·utilised to store firewood, this being loaded in from a ·r opening into the garden, while another door opening *the sitting-room* enables the logs to be thrown straight ·the hearth. Though we are not dependent on the wood ·for heat, we find it an additional winter comfort en-·ng, however, some extra work.

·ll the fitment furniture and panelling of the downstairs ·room is enamelled pale grey; and an artist friend has ·rated the panels with medallions of old-world ladies ·ned in soft lilac and rose. The Axminster carpeting is ·· and midnight blue, the same colours appearing in the ·ains. The wardrobe recess is furnished with patent ·ngs, which treble the hanging capacity of a wardrobe.

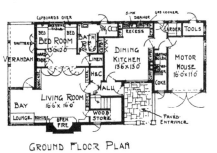

GROUND FLOOR PLAN

0   5   10   20   30   40 FEET

·covering curtain is secured *top and bottom* with rings. ·the space below is utilised for drawers. The bed adjoin-·the wardrobe is panelled to the ceiling.

·oth beds are fixtures, and fitted underneath with nests ·rawers. The cupboard fitments at the head of each bed

·n well ·ove the ·low line; ·e project-·cupboards ·as draught-·ens for the ·.

·he larger ·dow in the ·d room ·fitted with ·ide shutters ·· use in ·gorous ·ather; ·gh the ·ndah roof ·ents rain ·· driving ·t any time. ·· large linen ·pboard ·· has ad-·nal shelves ·hooks for ·hes.

·he bath-·n leads off ·bedroom, ·is tiled in

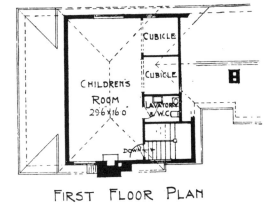

FIRST FLOOR PLAN

white and turquoise blue; a gutter (with outlet) runs round the black-and-blue mosaic floor, and the corners of the room are rounded (as elsewhere throughout the house) to avoid dust-traps. The room is heated with radiators. It has a hot towel-rail, and there is a cupboard under the washing basin, and glass shelves above. The taps are of special white enamel, so that there is no nickel or brass to clean.

In the curtained, white-tiled recess of the dining-room-kitchen is the sink (with a draining-board at each end), also an electric cooking-stove. A slate-topped table, which takes no hurt from hot pans, provides a cool surface for pastry-making. Above the sink are patent racks, into which cups, saucers, plates, and dishes can be placed after rinsing in clean water.

The shelves above the stove and table are of iron, with a specially prepared *white-enamelled surface*. These shelves, for cooking utensils, etc., were a "brain-wave" on the part of the architect, and made to his special order. They are excellent in every way. Two minutes' work a day means spotlessly clean shelves with a glossy white surface, which does not chip or crack. We use these shelves in the larder, too, where the tiny north window and the door panels are of perforated zinc, and a commodious ice-box proves a boon in summer.

The most fastidious need find nothing distasteful in par-taking of meals in this combination room, discreetly curtained. The sink and stove are spotless. No bits of any description are ever allowed to escape down the outlet. Over the sink is a window, and outside, within easy reach, hangs a bucket into which all bits from the plates can be emptied. Where coal and oil are abolished for cooking, pots and pans can be kept spick and span without any undue labour.

The curtain across the recess is secured with rings top and bottom (the lower rail being inset in the floor); this arrange-ment does away with the flapping nui-sance on windy days.

When a table serves several purposes, a white cloth, before even a meal begins, too often shows the stains and rims

Though heated with radiators the servantless house succumbed to tradition in having a fine open grate for the cheerful blaze of logs on cold days

Wireless for the *Home*

Some of the marvellous possibilities of Broadcasting, and its far-reaching effects upon our lives in the near future, are dealt with in this article, which explains how, among other achievements, wireless makes it possible to listen, in your own home, to an opera or concert taking place hundreds of miles away

By John Ellacott Genner

BROADCASTING! The newspapers talk about it daily, politicians and public men make statements upon the subject, but this abundance of information is either too technical to be comprehensible or so vague as to be quite meaningless to mere Man and Woman. There is vague talk about concerts and sound waves, about church sermons and antennæ, yet those who are supposed to benefit most by this innovation are those who know least about the subject. There has been a flood of misinformation, and extravagant claims, which have little or no foundation in fact, have been made.

That broadcasting will undoubtedly be welcomed by all, and in particular by those who value their homes, is not to be doubted, because it offers every encouragement for people to receive their entertainment within the comfort of their homes.

Broadcasting is, in reality, the sending out of messages from a central station through the ether—the name given to the medium through which radio waves travel—so that, with the aid of receiving apparatus in the home, everyone, within a certain area, can pick them up. These messages are not sent out in code, but are actually spoken into one or more special telephone transmitters, the shape of which is somewhat similar to a megaphone. The sound of the voice is carried, by means of very delicate and costly apparatus, into the air so that you may, with the assistance of your receiving apparatus, listen-in (that is the phrase for receiving the messages) and actually hear the voice of the speaker though he may be some hundreds—even thousands—of miles away.

It has been said that this invention is probably the nearest approach to a miracle that the world has known. Think of it: a voice travelling in space, unguided, to be picked up at will by anyone within a huge radius of miles! This is indeed the harnessing of the Air.

The use of the ether is by no means limitless. It will accommodate just so many wireless messages and no more. If this limit is exceeded, then chaos reigns and those who are listening-in with their receiving apparatus hear no more than one incessant conglomeration of noises and discordant sounds.

In order to control the broadcasting of wireless messages, the General Post Office are devising plans whereby Great Britain is to be divided into eight sectors with two transmitting stations in each. Permission to broadcast will therefore be limited to a total of sixteen concerns, and only those capable of giving really first-class transmission and service will receive licences for broadcasting. At the present moment the General Post Office are in negotiation with the various industrial concerns who have applied for permission to broadcast, and nothing in the way of definite information regarding organisation can be given until the end of their deliberations. That which interests most people, however, is the matter to be received and the method of receiving.

At the transmitting stations definite daily programmes will be arranged and information published each morning in the newspapers regarding the times of each performance. If you are interested in any item of the day's programme you listen-in and have all the enjoyment in your own armchair of a concert or lecture.

Many people, particularly women, are scared at the thought of anything electrical, because they do not understand the apparatus. There is the dread fear of "getting shocks." With wireless receiving sets there are no such possibilities of shocks—because they do not exist, and every member of the family, with a little practice, will be able to receive broadcasted messages from broadcasting transmitting stations.

Matter is broadcast from transmitting stations on a definite "wave-length," and before it is possible to pick up the sound on one's apparatus it is necessary to "tune up" to that particular sound-wave. This requires a little practice before the best results are obtainable and it is therefore most advisable in the first instance to purchase a Crystal Set with which to experiment and practice. The Crystal Set is not a highly delicate instrument, but sufficiently accurate to obtain satisfactory results.

This set is for use within a radius of twelve to twenty-five miles from the transmitting station, and is supplied complete in a polished mahogany case. Its cost is in the neighbourhood of £5, and certainly no instruments marketed at a price considerably lower are worth consideration.

In the same way that broadcasting is transmitted through an aerial, so must it be received through an aerial; and so this is really the first consideration of those who wish to broadcast at home. The aerial takes various forms, but the Indoor Aerial, as apart from the Outdoor Aerial, will probably be most suitable in this country owing to the comparatively limited garden space of most homes. The aerial for indoor use is merely a few yards of wire coiled round a small frame and can be strung up in an attic or placed conveniently in a living-room. This aerial is connected by a small covered wire to your Crystal Receiving Set, and when you have tuned up your apparatus you place the telephone receivers over your head and on to your ears, and, leaning back in your chair, you listen in comfort to whatever may be in course of broadcasting at that moment.

When the amateur has mastered this Crystal Set his interest will be greatly stimulated and his ambition will be to have a further receiving set of greater range and efficiency, and in purchasing the Valve Detector Set he has an apparatus of an altogether different quality. This set is both delicate and accurate, and will give uniformly better results.

families were thrown together far more, although they gave fathers an escape route into the garden.

New Horizons

Women's horizons were beginning to expand outside the kitchen too. The wireless brought news, music and educational 'talks' to women who had very little time to read the papers, superseding the piano and the gramophone as the focus of evening entertainment. By 1927, 3 million homes had a wireless. Women often listened to the radio all day long as they did their housework, and it came to dominate the pattern of family evenings at home. The telephone – installed in 1.6 million homes by 1929 – increased contact with the outside world, while the increasing popularity of the car introduced motoring as a pastime. Technology and Henry Ford's new production-line techniques brought car prices down, and advertisers emphasised to women the benefits of taking their children to school or shopping with the car. In the decade which also saw the extension of the vote to all women over 21, the decline of the birthrate to an unprecedentedly low level, rising hemlines and the advent of the uncorseted flapper girl, women were being promised more freedom than ever before.

Left: The wireless introduced millions of women to a wider world

the 1930s:

TEASMADES AND TELEVISION

THE 1930S WAS A DECADE OF CONTRADICTIONS. The early 1930s saw the worldwide great Depression, which hit Britain severely: unemployment was measured in millions, the gold standard was abandoned and sterling devalued, and strikes hit the country as pay was cut and income tax rose. During the latter part of the decade, the threat of war loomed and the government started planning conscription, rationing, mass issue of air-raid shelters and evacuation.

Yet at the same time the standard of living continued to rise for the middle classes. House building continued, with home ownership made more accessible by more widely available building society mortgages. Car ownership increased to around 2.5 million in 1936 (and the number of accidents soared correspondingly, too, until driving tests, traffic lights and road markings were introduced). And most importantly, the appliances which had been developed in the 1920s began to filter into homes in greater numbers. Although electricity was only enjoyed by just over half of the population – even by 1938 only 65 per cent of homes in Britain were wired up – by the end of the 1930s a range of 'labour saving' appliances and gadgets featured in most middle-class homes.

Gear-changing, ladies? Why, nothing simpler!

4-DOOR SALOON **£285**

(Ex Works, Hendon)

Flush-type weatherproof sliding roof, £10 extra.

Fixed-head Coupé - **£295**

All - weather Saloon and Drop-head Coupé - - **£325**

Special 26-h.p. model for overseas.

● **FAULTLESS GEAR - CHANGE**

No double declutching, no "feeling" for gears, no stalling, no noise — you never need make a bad gear-change on the Vauxhall Cadet. Synchro-Mesh gears give you a feeling of expert control; the Silent Second makes it pleasant to use your gears as you should. And in performance and appearance the Cadet is all you could wish for. Ask any dealer for a trial run, or write to General Motors Ltd., The Hyde, Hendon, London, N.W.9.

"WHAT do you think Daddy had the cheek to tell me?" inquired Sheila. "He said he got a Vauxhall Cadet this time so that I shouldn't make a row with the gears. I, mind you! When he himself used to make an awful clatter on the old car!"

"Too bad," responded Peter—always the dutiful fiancé. "Still," he added, thoughtfully, "whether he was studying you or himself,

he's picked a winner. I suppose you know this car's got Synchro-Mesh?"

"I didn't—but I'll tell you what I do know. I know that you don't have to double-declutch when you want to change down — you just move the lever, and there you are in second, without making a sound."

"Exactly," chuckled Peter. "That's what Synchro-Mesh does for you— besides giving you a quieter second gear than you've ever known before."

VAUXHALL CADET

(17 H.P. —— SIX CYLINDERS)

It's British

COMPLETE RANGE OF MODELS ON VIEW AT 174-182 GREAT PORTLAND STREET. LONDON. W.1

For the wealthiest families, the car brought great freedom

the turbulent thirties

1930   Fibreglass was first made in Britain

1931   There was a political crisis in Britain as the gold standard was abandoned, sterling was devalued, and unemployment reached a record high

Creda produced the first electric cooker with thermostatic control

1932   The Mars Bar was born

The first plastic radio set, the Ekco SH25 with a Bakelite case, went on sale

1933   Polythene and tampons were invented in the US

The first Anglepoise lamp was sold

1934   Driving tests were introduced

Cling film was invented

The first Vent-Axia extractor fan and the first Goblin Teasmade were made

1935   Perspex became available in the UK

1936   The Jarrow march

The speaking clock was introduced – and almost 250,000 calls were made in its first week

The first BBC television broadcast was made from Alexandra Palace

King Edward VIII abdicated

1937   Kit Kat bars were launched

The 999 emergency telephone service was introduced

Nylon was patented in the US

Smedley's asparagus was the first frozen food in Britain

1938   Teflon was discovered (by accident) during work on refrigerants

The first Y-fronts were sold (left-handers were advised to wear them inside out)

Instant coffee was developed

1939   The first-ever colour television and fridge with freezer compartment went on sale

War was declared on 3 September

...I'm not complaining!...I'm not nagging!...I'm just telling you!...I want £1 and I want it now!

● "I've had just about enough of working 12 hours a day while you're working 8—that is, if you don't take two hours for lunch . . . I don't want more money—I want less work . . . Look at your office—addressographs—adding machines—typewriters—extension phones—why, you don't even sharpen your pencils yourself . : . You're working in 1934 in your business, I'm working in 1834 . . . That's why I want £1!...I want just one home appliance that's going to lighten my work, that's going to shorten my day. I am sick and tired of struggling with old-fashioned methods that take four times as long, then only get a tenth of the dirt . . . I want a Hoover."

If you are tired of working with 1834 cleaning methods—broom and brush, duster and dustpan—send the coupon below, now, and learn all about the cleaning methods of the Hoover, and how it can be purchased for as low as **£1** down.

This was partly due to prices falling, especially after Britain imposed a 20 per cent import tax on foreign goods to encourage domestic trade, and companies such as Hoover and Electrolux began manufacturing in Britain on a large scale. In 1936, Morphy Richards began mass-producing smaller appliances such as kettles and toasters, using American-style production-line techniques which cut prices by around 40 per cent. The widespread introduction of hire-purchase schemes also made appliances accessible to more people: advertisers tempted women with the chance to own a brand-new Hoover or electric fire for just 'a pound down'. Ownership of telephones, meanwhile, was rising by almost 300,000 per year. Appliances were so popular that the *Good Housekeeping* Institute was persuaded by readers to hold courses on the use of domestic equipment, and these ran throughout the 1930s.

Home Comforts

Trends in home building developed, with the emphasis on neat semis and detached houses with well-proportioned rooms, bathrooms and light kitchens. Being smaller, these houses were easier to keep warm, which must have made an enormous

Electric radiators emitting a non-scorching heat are used in the bed-room. The reflectors are of lacquered copper and ensure a cheerful glow

The All

By

N. L. Gall

In the sitting-room is an electric heat-er in imitation of a coal fire. Con-cealed cornice lighting supplements electric floor and table standards

Another model of the electric radiator in the bedroom. It serves as a table

Good Housekeeping Institute
49 Wellington Street, Strand, W.C.2
Conducted by
D. D. Cottington Taylor
Certificate of King's College of Household and Social Science; First Class
Diplomas in Cookery, High Class Cookery, Laundrywork, Housewifery, A.R.S.I.

MR. H. G. WELLS in his *Short History of the World* has given us in a nutshell, and with characteristic pungency, a history of electricity. He writes: "Concurrently with the de-velopment of steam transport upon land and sea a new and striking addition to the facilities of human intercourse arose out of the investigations of Volta, Galvani and Faraday into various elec-trical phenomena. The electric tele-graph came into existence in 1835. The first underseas cable was laid in 1851 between France and England. These things were to the popular imagination of the middle nineteenth century the most striking and revolutionary of in-ventions, but they were only the most

conspicuous and clumsy first-fruits of a far more extensive process. . . . It was only in the eighties of the nine-teenth century that this body of in-quiry began to yield results to impress the vulgar mind. Then suddenly came electric light and electric traction and the transmutation of forces, the possi-bility of sending *power,* that could be changed into mechanical motion or light or heat as one chose, along a copper wire, as water is sent along a pipe, began to come through to the ideas of ordinary people. . . ."

The average town-dweller of to-day with his well-ordered though rushed existence does not, perhaps, stop to con-sider what this "addition to the faci-lities of human intercourse" means to

him. He can sit at home and send his voice across the continents, he can touch a switch and obtain for himself all domestic amenities, while beyond his home sphere he may be transported from place to place quickly and cleanly. Speed and cleanliness are in fact the two greatest blessings brought by elec-tricity to the world at large, and the home in particular.

The all-electric house, like the all-gas house recently discussed in this magazine is a practical and in many cases an economical proposition. Two systems of selling electricity are in common use. With the first, one rate obtains for lighting and another and generally far cheaper one for all other domestic purposes.

This arrangement entails the use of two meters and two wiring circuits, a point overcome by the second system, in which case one meter and one wiring circuit only is required, the charge for all current consumed and for whatever purpose, being uniform.

Most people are familiar with the fact that electricity is measured in units, a unit consisting of the pressure or "voltage" of the electricity multiplied by the volume of flow or "amperage," multiplied by the time in hours for which it is used. By multiplying the "volts" by the "amps," the "watts" are computed, one thousand watts be-ing known as a kilowatt, commonly

Household Engineering & Housecraft

Good

Housekeeping

encouraged its

readers to

convert to

electricity

Cleanliness and efficiency are outstanding points in the all-electric kitchen, which is equipped with, among other things, an electrically operated refrigerator, electric cooker, water heater and clothes boiler

Electric
House

On the electric cooker specially constructed saucepans and kettles should be used

...ssed kw., and termed the ...ng" or "loading" of the appliance. ... a small article, such as a lamp ...ed "40 watts," consumes one unit ...5 hours; a comparatively large ...nce, such as an electric fire with ...ding of 1,000 watts or one kw., ...our only. Thus it may be seen that ...onsumer can readily reckon for ...lf the cost of using any electric ...nce. In making a true reckoning

of this cost there are other factors which should be considered. The entire cleanliness of all electric appliances minimises time and labour and effects economy in the hiring of domestic labour, and the wear and tear of the home.

In the all-electric house a generous number of points should be provided, and their positions carefully planned. Skirting and plug points in each room

may be used in connection with numerous appliances—vacuum cleaner, floor polisher, fan, kettle, toaster, wireless set and sewing machine, to mention but a few. In the garage such a point is useful for an inspection lamp, soldering iron or heater.

For lighting arrangements two-way controls are a great convenience, as for example, to light or extinguish a porch lamp from the hall, a lamp at the top of the stairs from the bottom, etc. Electric lighting is basically dependent for its efficiency on the lamp—a point which on the face of it seems too obvious for mention. It is, however, remarkable how little attention the average user pays to the particular type of lamp, its rating, and whether clear, frosted, or opalescent, he employs for a particular purpose. In a large number of cases the fitting and shade receive the attention, the latter often extremely detrimental to efficient illumination even by the right type of lamp. The two should always be considered together, for suitable fittings in conjunction with the right lamp produce efficiency with economy.

Electric heating possesses the outstanding advantage of portability. An electric fire requires no fitting and no flue, for there are no products of combustion to be removed from the room. One fire may also be used to heat various rooms, thus effecting economy in outlay. Heat control is simple and speedy, and practically instantaneous in its effect. These advantages should be taken into (*Continued on page* **178**)

43

A small table cooker is invaluable in the all-electric house. Eggs and bacon, tomatoes, chops and other similar dishes can be satisfactorily cooked on the plate on which they are served

The All-Electric House

(*Continued from page* **43**)

consideration when weighing the pros and cons of this type of heating. When choosing an electric fire a rough estimate as to a satisfactory loading may be made by allowing 1 to 1½ watts per cubic foot of space it is required to warm. Thus for a room approximately 12 feet by 10 feet by 9 feet high a 1 kw. fire would be required. It must be remembered, however, that the aspect of the room, the number of windows, etc. are of account in arriving at a really satisfactory conclusion. In any case it is well to err on the generous side as most fires have "low" and "medium" control switches. In large rooms it will often be found that two small fires are more economical and effective than one large one. If arrangement for so doing is made when wiring a house, fires may be controlled from several points, such as the bedside—a facility often of great convenience.

Electric fires are of several kinds to meet all requirements. The lightest and therefore most easily portable are those with sheet metal frames—a very wide selection with various finishes being obtainable. Those with cast iron frames are naturally heavier, but may be finished in vitreous enamel of various colours. Imitation coal fires are particularly popular for they are of pleasant appearance, both when on and off circuit, the glowing fuel effect being obtainable independently of the heat. These fires are made in many designs, a number having a reflector back plate on which the light plays with flickering fire effect. "Period" models are much in evidence with this type of fire. In places where space-saving is of importance, and in bathrooms, a wall-mounted fire is the best choice. When fixed in a bathroom the fire should be earthed and wired direct, and not connected to the circuit by a length of flex. For supplying a small amount of local heat a pedestal heater with bowl reflector is inexpensive and efficient.

Mention must also be made of a rather different type of electric radiator, the elements of which consist of one or more luminous lamps according to size, some large models for room heating having an additional heating element of the usual resistance wires. As will be seen from the picture of the bedroom illustrated, the warmth is downwardly-directed through louvre-like slots, the reflectors being of polished copper. Many models of this type of radiator are available, some in the form of circular or rectangular tables, others as floor standards with a small tray or table at a convenient height for holding a cup and saucer, ash-tray or book.

Central heating of the all-electric house may be by means of convectors for air warming, fitted with low temperature heating elements, or by electrically-heated hot water radiators.

The heating of water for general use is most economically done by the storage type of heater, although for small quantities of water instantaneous heaters are available. A storage heater consists essentially of an inner water container encased in heat-insulating material, enclosed within an outer casing; the heating apparatus, and an automatic temperature-controlling device or thermostat. This construction ensures the maximum against heat losses, and the elements, being of the immersion type, are totally surrounded by water, to which all the heat is transferred. The heaters are made in many sizes from those of about 1½ gallons capacity for fixing over washbasins or sinks, to those of large capacity to supply all taps through-

out the house. They may be finished in white enamel, chromium or nickel plate.

Existing installations may be wholly or partially converted to electricity by the introduction of immersion heaters into the hot water storage tank. The heaters are made to fit tanks of all shapes and sizes, and are fitted with three-heat switches for detailed control of temperature. Thus "low heat" may be left on during the night to ensure the morning supply of hot water, or at times when demands are small; other controls can be used when demands are greater or hot water more quickly required. The heaters are so constructed and fitted to the tank that they can be removed for inspection, etc., without the necessity for emptying the tank or in any way interfering with the heating system. This method of heating water is particularly useful as a supplement to another system, and for use in summer when a solid fuel boiler or fire is not desirable. To prevent heat losses, it is advisable with this type of heating to lag the tank or cylinder, and wherever possible, the pipes. Slag wool, crushed cork, felt, etc. are all suitable non-conducting materials, even corrugated cardboard serving the purpose quite satisfactorily. A very simple wood framing completes the insulation.

Cooking, by reason of the great variety of equipment available, is perhaps the most elastic of all services offered by electricity. From the large range to the small kettle, toaster, or boiling ring there are cookers of all sizes and kinds, and independent appliances for practically every cooking process. Ranges are of either the vertical or horizontal type, the latter having both oven and hot-plate elevated, prevents unnecessary stooping. Boiling plates are in most cases of the enclosed type to avoid damage to the elements by spilt liquids, etc., and like the ovens are fitted with three-heat control switches. Plate-warming is generally provided for beneath the hotplate, this space serving also to accommodate the grilling pan. An additional warming cupboard is provided above the oven in the horizontal models. Automatic control of oven temperature and enclosed elements are other features that aid cooking. Vitreous enamel, both durable and easily cleaned, is the general finish of all but some of the very small cookers.

The all-electric house can, with the minimum of inconvenience, achieve table cooking whether in the kitchen or dining-room. There are small "boiler-grillers" resembling a miniature hot-plate and oven with drop door, one element with three-heat control serving them both. Such an appliance is especially useful for supplementary cooking, to prepare or heat a small meal after a theatre, etc., or for the girl living alone. Somewhat larger table cookers designed for general use for a family of two or three are constructed on the same principle but have an additional oven element and side-hinged door. There are also small cookers especially made for dining-table use, and having a plated finish. On some a complete meal may be cooked, all processes, boiling, baking, frying and toasting being possible. One particularly compact uni-process cooker is designed to fit completely over the plate or dish, and thus wasting of heat or splashing of fat on the table is rendered impossible. Other single purpose table appliances include the always popular kettles, some of which are provided with a cut-out whereby the current is automatically switched off should the kettle be allowed to boil dry, and others with

These Radiants are
Inclined....
and that makes all the difference in the World!

difference to home comfort. They were usually supplied with electricity and gas, and heating with both fuels was beginning to take over from open fires – small electric fires were popular because they could be carried from room to room, and the first 'coal effect' fires were introduced to meet the demand for a warm-looking focal point. Instant hot water was also becoming a reality for more people thanks to gas and electric geysers and immersion heaters. Full central-heating systems were still very rare.

The look of kitchens continued to change as they were designed with new appliances in mind. Thought was also given for the first time to the ergonomics of kitchen design: a scientific approach was taken to the way in which the housewife performed basic tasks so that, for instance, the sink could be positioned more efficiently in relation to the cooker.

The Commercial Gas Association continued its hard sell to the housewife

Furniture was becoming more streamlined, lino floors were popular, and aluminium and Pyrex became more affordable thanks to mass production. From 1934 the first advertisements for metal sinks appeared, made from Savestane and Monel, an alloy similar to stainless steel but thicker and more expensive. They were beyond the means of most people; cheaper but chippable enamelled sinks were more typical, and still an improvement on porcelain or stone.

The 1930s household had one other addition – the dustbin. As open fires were phased out, housewives were left with a lot of rubbish on their hands. Galvanised iron dustbins were the solution, leading to regular refuse collection by local councils. An alternative was the waste-disposal unit, produced for the first time in 1935, but this was noisy and costly, and didn't prove popular. Gas and electricity continued to battle for supremacy, and the Commercial Gas Association replaced stuffy old Mr G A Service with Mr Therm, a cute little cartoon figure who promised warmth and comfort in the home. Gas remained the most

popular choice for cooking and heating – by 1939 there were 9.5 million gas cookers compared with 1 million electric, despite the invention of the thermostat for electric ovens – but the efficiency of electricity was undeniable, particularly for smaller appliances.

In technological terms, the 1930s was a time of refinement compared with the massive innovations of the 1920s. The basic workings of most appliances stayed the same; now it was a question of streamlining. Cosmetic concerns came to the fore, and large appliances were now offered in a range of coloured enamel finishes, introducing the idea of a colour-co-ordinated kitchen. Both gas and electric cookers become more streamlined, were fully enamelled and better insulated (unfortunately often with asbestos). The electric washing machine was improving, although hand-operated

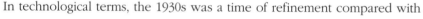

**The Good
Housekeeping
Institute gave
its seal of
approval to this
early
dishwasher**

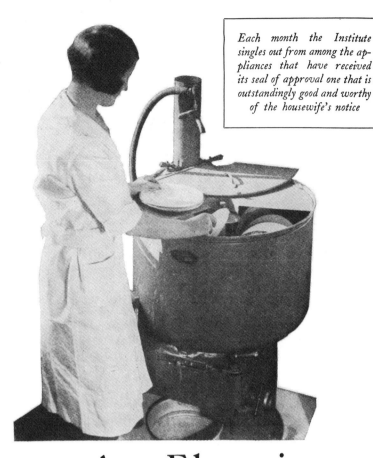

*Each month the Institute
singles out from among the appliances that have received
its seal of approval one that is
outstandingly good and worthy
of the housewife's notice*

An Electric
Dish Washer

The Month's Approved Appliance

THE very mention of dish washing spells drudgery, and any equipment designed for easing this task is sure of appreciation on the part of the housewife. In the large household of ten or twelve, a tremendous amount of washing-up accumulates after every meal, and one or two maids may easily be fully occupied attending to this for an hour or so.

In such establishments or small institutions, a small electrically operated dishwasher would save a tremendous amount of time and labour. The machine illustrated was used in Good Housekeeping Institute for washing-up luncheon and tea things for twenty people. It was found that the luncheon plates and dishes could be washed by one instead of two maids in about one hour, whereas it had previously occupied two maids this length of time.

The maid responsible for the washing-up was able to effect further saving of time by carrying out other household duties such as folding and ironing laundry-work, collecting tea things, etc., while the machine was in operation.

The various tests carried out proved that dishes not longer than twelve inches could be satisfactorily washed, while as many as thirty plates could be washed at a time.

It was found in practice that it was generally more satisfactory to interspace about twenty plates with cups and saucers, as each individual piece was then washed more thoroughly. Twelve cups, saucers, and plates could be accommodated at a time, the cups being placed in the machine in an inverted position.

It was noted that the machine was more suitable for larger articles, than for knives, spoons and forks, etc., as these, though carefully packed, tended to drop through the basket into the container during the washing process.

The average amount of water used for washing one load was three gallons, and we found that the use of a little soda or soap powder was advisable when washing greasy dishes.

This machine is simple in construction, consisting of a rotating galvanised wire basket for holding the crockery, which is mounted in a circular container supported on a cylindrical stand in which is enclosed an insulated hot water storage tank, heated by an electric immersion heater. The tank is connected by means of pipes and control cocks with the main cold water supply in such a way that hot water or a mixture of hot and cold water can be discharged under

It sounds too good to be true!

Incredible—but at last a fact! We here introduce to the world a servant guaranteed to do all the heavy washing and cleaning in your home without ever giving notice! Without ever needing a day off or a night out; mood-proof and even tantrum-proof. This paragon is ATMOS "The Mechanical Housemaid"! At your constant service, to boil clothes (by a *new* and cleaner method), wring them (as easily as turning a mincer), dry them, and provide for the ironing of them; to vacuum clean your home from top to bottom; to do, in short, everything from the week's wash to boiling a kettle!

IT WASHES CLOTHES

IT BLUES OR DYES THEM

IT DRIES THEM

VACUUM CLEANS

'ATMOS' *The Mechanical Housemaid*

A Clothes Washer; Rinser; Wringer; Drier; Ironer—and a Vacuum Cleaner

Send for your FREE Copy of the ATMOS booklet giving you all the miraculous details—plus your nearest address for demonstrations. All feminine England is going to go wild about the ATMOS.

BURSLEM'S PATENTS LIMITED, BANK BUILDINGS, 20, KINGSWAY, LONDON, W.C.2

tubs continued to sell well (and were cheaper). The electric variety now generally had a metal rather than wooden tub, housed in square-sided casing, with an enamel finish, an 'agitator' mechanism, and a hand-wringer on the top. Most significantly, they dropped in price

The 'electric servant', a combined food mixer and washing machine, was not a great success

from around £42 in 1926 to around £20 in 1936. Refrigerators, still a relative luxury item, became smaller (shrinking from 13 square feet to 5 square feet between 1926 and 1936) and quieter as motors were improved.

Electrical gadgets were becoming much more user-friendly: the food mixer, for instance, looked very similar to those we use today; as did the toaster. The Goblin Teasmade – the height of luxury for housewives used to early-morning tea-making in a chilly kitchen – was developed in 1934.

The 1930s saw two quite remarkable innovations which sadly failed to take the world by storm. The Thor 'electric servant', which the Good Housekeeping Institute recommended to readers in 1936, not only washed clothes, but doubled up as a food mixer, beater and juicer. There is no mention of clothes emerging covered in cake mix, or fruit juice tasting of Persil, but for whatever reason the machine didn't become a best-seller. Nor did the Atmos, described as a 'mechanical housemaid': a 'Clothes washer; rinser; wringer; drier; ironer – and a vacuum cleaner'! The manufacturers claimed, 'All feminine England is going to go wild about the Atmos.' They didn't. But

At 100 guineas, the first television sets cost more than a small car.

the makers of these bizarre machines were well ahead of their time: even today the all-purpose domestic machine is still in the realms of science fiction.

While technology continued to improve, patterns of family life were also changing more rapidly as more middle-class families moved into the new suburbs. The new houses usually had gardens and garages: men began to tinker outside with their cars, and gardening became a new hobby. Indoors, the wireless reached into

Do you use to full

By

N. L. Gall

An example of the new hand combination set. This model, in ivory, is designed for use in provincial districts, where it is only necessary to dial the number

Alexander Graham Bell, the inventor of the telephone. An interesting point about this photograph is the fact that the original was transmitted from San Francisco to New York (3,305 miles) over a telephone wire in under eight minutes

IF everyone studied the introductory pages of the telephone directory, much of this article would have no excuse for having been written.

But who studies these pages? Who knows, among many other and more important things, that he or she, like the telephone operator, is requested as a "useful precaution" against being misunderstood, to say "fife" and not five, or that for the same excellent reason a short pause should be made between the hundreds and tens when asking for a number? These particular remarks apply, of course, to the users of the manual telephone and not to those of the automatic system which is gradually superseding it.

The preface to the telephone directory is a veritable mine of useful information. It should be studied by the competent telephone user in much the same manner as the competent cook studies her book of recipes, knowing full well that neither can obtain the best results for her efforts by mere guesswork, and that without such study much will be left undone through lack of knowledge.

The telephone system is now a colossal organisation and, at the time of writing, plans are being made for a huge advertising campaign still further to increase its popularity.

Its present magnitude may be grasped to some extent by the fact that there are 2,000,000 telephones in this country and 34,000,000 all over the world.

There are more than 4,760 telephone exchanges in this country, 1,252,000 miles of overhead wire and 7,587,000 miles of underground wire. Approximately 33,350 call offices and kiosks are also in existence.

In London the cost of the telephone is 2s. 6d. per week, in Manchester, Liverpool, Birmingham and Glasgow 2s. 4d. per week, and in all other places 2s. 1½d. Business premises have an additional charge made of 7s. 6d. per quarter. Local calls cost one penny each, others according to distance, and the time at which the call is made.

Reduced charges are in force for distance calls between 2 p.m. and 7 p.m., while between 7 p.m. and 7 a.m. the charge for a three-minute call is generally half that for the morning period.

There is perhaps no public service more consistently criticised than this of the telephone, but, as the opening words of that excellent preface are careful to tell you, "There are three parties to a telephone call: yourself, the exchange, the distant subscriber"; is it not possible that blame for faulty operation should sometimes attach itself to any one of the parties mentioned, and not invariably and of indisputable necessity to one only?

It must not be thought that these or any following remarks are an attempt to whitewash the Post Office in connection with its telephone service, or are sponsored by instigators of a "telephone more" or any similar campaign. They are merely intended to remind the subscriber of the ways in which he can assist efficient service, and obtain the full facilities available.

Much of the annoyance felt towards the telephone service by the manual telephone user is caused by "wrong numbers" both received and given. There can be no doubt that this difficulty would be overcome to a large extent if each subscriber were more careful to give the number required in the right way, *i.e.* to give figures which are liable to become blurred or mistaken for others the pronunciation recommended by the Post Office and to

the TELEPHONE *advantage*?

Many subscribers may not be aware of all the facilities that the telephone service offers and will be glad to have the points in this article brought to their notice

A telephone table designed to fit over the arm of a chair enables dial telephoning to be accomplished in comfort

A general view of one of the newest automatic exchanges: these eliminate the use of telephone operators as an electric current finds the number

separate the hundreds and tens as already mentioned. The word " double " —that bane of so many telephone users— should be employed when the double figure comes before or after the dividing pause, and not when it occurs in the middle of the number, *i.e.* 6662 should be referred to as double six, six two; not six double six two.

When trouble is experienced in making any particular word clear the various letters or any one of them can be readily understood by such analogy as G for George, U for uncle, etc. These simple methods will often avoid misunderstanding or irritation through delay caused by wrong numbers. Time would also invariably be saved if that

most popular of all answers to the telephone bell, " Hullo," were dropped in favour of the name of the subscriber or business house concerned.

The coming of the automatic system seems to be unnecessarily dreaded by many telephone users. Their particular fear appears to be that they will not be able to distinguish the various audible signals called " tones," which are used in place of the information previously given by the exchange operator. There is, however, nothing formidable or confusing about these tones once they are heard and remembered. The continuous burr-rr-rr of the " dialling tone," indicating that dialling may be commenced, is quite distinct from the

divided burr-burr of the " ringing tone," when the number required is being rung. These tones are again entirely different from the buzzing noises which indicate that the number is engaged or unobtainable.

The actual dialling requires nothing beyond a little practice to obtain speed, and the knowledge that the first three letters only of the exchange required (which are printed in heavy type in the directory) must be dialled, followed by the numerals.

Full instructions on these and all other points connected with the automatic telephone are given in the directory preface, and if carefully followed little or no trouble should be experienced.

It is very doubtful if all telephone users are aware of the extent to which they can employ their telephone. The personal call service is one of the most recent facilities. It enables a trunk, toll or international call to be booked to a specified person or his substitute, or if preferred two numbers may be given, at either of which the person desired may be found. Such personal calls are only connected when the person to whom it is desired to speak (or his specified substitute) is obtained. The extra charge for this service is from 1s. to 2s., according to distance, from 7 a.m. to 2 p.m.; and 6d., regardless of distance, between 2 p.m. and 7 a.m.

ever more homes, with new lightweight Bakelite sets becoming popular. Later in the decade came the radiogram, which combined wireless and gramophone (now driven by an electric motor rather than a wind-up mechanism) in one large wooden cabinet. The radiogram became a focal point of many living rooms and was turned into a stylish piece of furniture, often made in walnut, oak and even ebony, costing from 30 to 50 guineas. Cinema-going was still a popular form of family entertainment, with statistics suggesting that 40 per cent of the population went to the cinema once a week.

The Birth of Television

Although its impact was delayed by the war, the end of the decade saw the development of the one appliance which has perhaps brought about the biggest upheaval in family life in the twentieth century – television. The first British broadcast was made from Alexandra Palace in 1936, but, at 100 guineas, a television set was more expensive than a small car. By 1939 sets cost under £50; however, the service was still only available to 10,000 homes around Alexandra Palace. War brought transmission to a halt, and it would be another decade before television became truly accessible.

Despite, or perhaps because of, all of these developments – easier-to-care-for houses and a range of appliances at their disposal – housewives were encountering a new problem. In 1938 doctors reported the phenomenon of 'suburban neurosis', experienced by housewives cut off from their old communities and their families. The problems of the lonely suburban wife, carrying out her mechanised tasks without even a maid to talk to, were often coyly referred to as 'nerves', and nerve tonics such as Sanatogen were advertised as antidotes. But by the end of the decade, as preparations were made for war and *Good Housekeeping* swung its weight behind the war effort, the psychological troubles of the housewife were pushed firmly into the background.

You can forget the dinner . . .

It's cooking itself in the NEW WORLD with the 'REGULO' CONTROL

Automatic Cooking—that is one of the advantages you gain by using the "New World" Gas Cooker with its 'Regulo' oven-heat control. Even complete dinners can be cooked simultaneously without any attention, and numerous suitable menus are available.

The "New World" is economical, too, due to its single oven burner and direct bottom-flue-outlet. Cooking also is *better*, the food is more appetizing, more tasty.

And the Gas Match enables you to light the burners without the bother of matches.

"New World" Gas Cookers with their shining porcelain-enamel finish are easily cleaned and keep their attractive appearance. Your Gas Showrooms can give you full particulars. Post the coupon below for Free Recipe Book.

'Regulo'-controlled NEW WORLD GAS COOKERS
Radiation LTD.

NEW WORLD
Series 2

Radiation

COUPON FOR FREE RECIPE BOOKLET

To : *Radiation Ltd.* (Publications Dept. 42 C), 164, *Queen Victoria Street, London, E.C.*4

Please send your free Recipe Book.

Name_____

Address_____

In the 1930s gas ovens became more sophisticated in their controls

★ *GOOD HOUSEKEEPING MOTORING SECTION* ★

A WOMAN NEEDS A CAR

It keeps her out of a domestic rut and adds much to life

says

GILLIAN MAUD

ANOTHER Motor Show is almost with us. How time flies! Everything on this earth goes in cycles, even cars and horses and other means of personal road transportation. How many of us, I wonder, realise that with the present acceptance of women as responsible motorists—and even the most hard-boiled he-man must admit that women at the wheel have proved themselves the equal of men—we are back to mediæval times? That is not so silly as it sounds. For many a generation we weak, must-be-protected beings have been steered or conveyed with tutelary complaisance by our strong and not-always-so-silent consorts or patriarchs.

One can assume with safety and logic that the average reader of GOOD HOUSE-KEEPING is a woman of means; she is able at least to afford a car of some kind. In mediæval times, women of means were nothing like so numerous in proportion to our population as they are to-day. They travelled as their men folk travelled, astride a horse, on a basis of equality in dexterity, stamina and endurance. With the passing of the centuries, however, things in this particular altered.

This delving into history has much to do with a consideration of motoring in this and the coming year. A wee bit of reflection will help us to comprehend that, having returned, at last, to a position parallel with our husbands and brothers in transport matters, we still have quite a long way to go before we make full use of our emancipation.

Perhaps post-mediæval women became less sturdy and more susceptible to fatigue, perchance their lords and masters (how fatuous that looks in cold print to-day) thought that the time had come to call a halt to their freedom of movement. Be that as it may, the later Middle Ages found the fair sex in "ladies' carriages," contraptions that would have shamed present-day farm carts as regards suspension systems and general comfort. Then followed the "litter," which was nothing more nor less than a glorified, canopied, four-poster bed slung on a pole and carried by man or beast. Even ladies of royal blood were expected to travel in this lumbering, unhealthy way.

Later came stage wagons, private coaches and sedan chairs. Many of us can remember the lighter forms of horse-drawn

vehicles that were the vogue down to the days of our grandparents—the dog-carts, the landaus, the cabriolets and the traps, and we can recollect also that precious few women were allowed to take the reins.

In the early days of motoring, the tiller—and later the steering wheel—responded only to the movements of masculine hands. But for the war, when women took over almost every civilian male activity, it is probable that motoring, other than that of passive participation from the passenger seats, would still be a male prerogative. Women, even at the beginning of motoring, were itching to "take over," but I will defy anyone to provide a picture, published prior to the Coronation of King George the Fifth, showing a woman in control of a car. No man would admit that any woman *could* drive. Medical reports show that insanity is decreasing. Probably

It is human to sigh with envy when a super-limousine slinks up and disgorges its opulent freight

this is due to the fact that many people, mostly women, who were considered crazy several years ago are now able to smile and say, "I told you so."

Congested traffic holds no terrors for the women drivers of 1938; on the open road they show a clean pair of heels—or is it bumpers?—to their male counterparts; they compete with success in reliability trials and high speed racing on the tracks of the world. No longer does the family car remain cloistered in its garage until the omnipotent expert returns from his place of business. Only the most timid of matrons refuses to take the wheel of to-day; if there is a car in the family, and the family is a matey one, it is used more by the feminine members than by the head (?) of the house. But . . . there are not enough car-owning families, certainly the number of two-car families is far too small. Thousands of business and professional men who use their cars genuinely for purposes connected with the winning of the daily bread, or selfishly for running merely to and from their offices, can afford a second car yet deny the home team the benefits that one would confer.

If a woman is to live a *full* life to-day she needs a car during the daytime. No longer is a car a luxury. As every woman knows, who has ever had a car to use whenever her whims dictated, it is a definite necessity. It is a far cry from the days of the horseless carriage, when a box of tricks that was nothing more than a landau propelled by an unreliable engine (instead of being pulled by a consistently dependable horse) cost a mint of money. To-day all cars are trustworthy, simple to manage and, according to one's individual tastes, economical to buy and maintain.

It is only human to sigh with envy as some long, lithe, super-limousine slinks silently and majestically to the portico of a luxury hotel or disgorges its opulent freight at a theatre. Some of us *may* be able to afford such creations, but everything is relative, and a car costing, say, £200 can be just as reliable, almost as fast and quite as satisfying in our sphere of life as an expensive giant that is in keeping only with the predilections of a plutocrat.

The modern housewife needs a car of her own if she cannot use the family car during the day. Household equipment, even in these days of inadequate domestic staffs,

In the early days the motor's tiller responded only to masculine hands

lightened home duties to such an extent leisure is delightfully increased, and re must be used properly if one is to d stagnation. A car can mean so much ne's life. Hubby, assuming that he is the selfish type who considers the train he beneath his dignity, can be put on 8.45 and met off the 6.50. The young-s can be taken to school (probably e desirable one than " St. Watisit's," e adjacent, to which they could walk); ping can be done on the way back, and much nicer it is to choose one's joint uit or vegetables instead of trusting to and the telephone!

visit to the dressmaker can be taken ne's stride, a few sets of tennis or a er of bridge encompassed in a day , carless, would have been impossible. riet's birthday can be acknowledged a heartening call instead of a soulless ting card; Mary and her new arrival ted in the nursing home with a bunch lowers and a smile instead of one of colourful telegram forms so thought-y provided by the postal authorities. A can help one in a thousand little ways get and keep out of a domestic rut— the only differences between a rut and roove are in the width and depth—not will it smooth out every day, but le one to put more into every day out fatigue.

is very disquieting to read that there a drop of 7,919 in the number of new registered during June compared with e last year. Those were the last official res published and, to me, they indicate husbands have gone all economical or es are not standing up for their rights! tainly unmarried motorists, men and nen, are not holding back in the buying irst or new cars.

here is no dearth of money in Britain sport or for the average small things life. It is only when facing possible ments of large single items that our d-winners announce the need for omy. If hubby does believe that there omething obscure happening called a ness recession, the last thing for ch he should be parsimonious is the vision of daily enjoyment and ease of ing about for the rest of the family.

If people stop buying cars, the men who make those cars will not be able to buy the things they need for their families; demand will fall for all kinds of things and then there *will* be a recession—or call it by its proper, uncamouflaged name—a slump. Meanwhile more money is being earned and saved than for many a year. Savings banks are overloaded with deposits. Something is wrong somewhere, folks are going slow who need not go slow. The motor industry is one of the greatest and most important in Britain; on its prosperity depends much of the prosperity of the whole country and on its products depend much of the happiness and freedom from inertia of we who run the substantial homes of the country. I repeat, no married woman amongst the readers of GOOD HOUSEKEEPING should be without a car.

A car should be treated as a domestic appliance; to get the best value out of it it should be used, used whenever opportunity permits, and just as we learn how to look after our sweepers, and our radios and our refrigerators and cookers, so should we understand how to treat our cars so that they will give the same trouble-free service. Incidentally, the last person from whom to learn driving is hubby. Either he will assume that you *must* be dull or else he will know that you are wonderful. Either way he will leave too much for granted. You need to know what to do and, just as important, why you do it when learning to take the wheel, control a car and become an expert and confident roadfarer. A good school of motoring gives by far the best tuition.

Your idea of a car's usefulness may be its place in the daily round of pottering about, an aid to social intercourse—a means for whisking a tea hamper and the family away into green fields and God's fresh air for a picnic. Maybe you look upon a car, as did our forefathers with their smart conveyances, as a mark of caste; perhaps you like to let off steam and refresh jaded nerves by an exhilarating dash along arterial roads. Your inclinations may lean towards roomy comfort, smartness of line, speed or economy. There are cars to suit every taste and every purse, some that shine in one particular attribute, some that combine all desires. The best place to see all types of cars together and the only spot where the offerings of all the makers are to be found in one complete gathering is the Motor Exhibition at Earl's Court. It opens on October 13th. It is the only time in the whole year when it is possible to

view such a galaxy of cars, from the "babies" to the juggernauts. I advise every woman who can possibly get there to pay a visit. It is useless looking at everything but, having decided just how much can be squeezed out of the family budget for a new car one can examine and discuss all those that are in the price range (one usually exceeds the agreed figure), and then having narrowed down the choice

If the family is a matey one, the car is used more by the feminine members

to a sensible few, one can arrange for trial runs in one's own locality. That is the way to make the final decision. Whether you go to Earl's Court this year or whether you stay away, remember, that to every woman of moderate means and tastes a car is an absolute necessity if life is to be made to yield all that it offers. There is so much to do to-day that cannot be done without a car that can be available always; and . . . running a car, like running a home, is easy and safe. This may sound elementary and very, very obvious, but the fact remains that thousands of young matrons and eager girls approaching marriageable age are living unnecessarily circumscribed lives because of their inability to keep pace with the times . . . a woman *needs* a car.

The youngsters can be taken to school—a more desirable one than " St. Watisit's " just next door

the 1940s:

JAM TOMORROW

THE HUGE TECHNOLOGICAL ADVANCES MADE in the home during the 1920s and 1930s came to an abrupt halt with the outbreak of war. The development of domestic appliances was virtually abandoned as all Britain's resources were focused on the war effort: metal production was geared entirely towards making planes, ships and armaments, and the manufacture of fridges, washing machines and cookers was at the bottom of the list of priorities. In 1942, the buying and selling of new cars was banned, as was driving for pleasure, to save fuel. Having been exhorted to use more gas and electricity in their homes before the war, housewives were now encouraged to save them: hints from the Ministry of Fuel and Power included using only one bar on the electric fire, cooking on the smallest gas ring and never using more than 5 inches of water in the bath. Spending money on what few consumer products existed was now considered unpatriotic: women were encouraged to spurn the 'Squander Bug' and support the war effort by buying National Savings Certificates instead.

The war fought on the home front by British housewives involved making do and mending, and eking out meagre rations to feed the family. Combining paid

Air Raid Wardens appreciate the Super-Fast Burner

Not the least of the time-saving features of the modern Regulo New World Gas Cooker is the super-fast burner which boils 1 pint of water in 125 secs! Other refinements for better, quicker and more economical cooking include a high-speed grill reaching toasting heat in 60 secs. Unique oven design with single burner; and, of course, the *genuine* '*Regulo*'— which automatically saves gas and enables a complete meal to be perfectly cooked all at the same time. OVER 2 MILLIONS IN DAILY USE.

REGULO NEW WORLD

GAS COOKERS

SEE THEM AT YOUR GAS SHOWROOMS

See the Cooking Number in the REGULO TRIANGLE ▲

A **Radiation** product

To Radiation Ltd., Publications Dept. 56,
7 Stratford Place, London, W.1.
Please send free Recipe Book with 'Regulo' Marks (½d. stamp only if envelope is unsealed)

Name_____

COUPON   Address_____

Even advertisements for cookers became part of the war effort

the austere forties

1940 Wartime measures included food rationing, a government ban on buying and selling new cars, and a 24 per cent tax on luxury goods

The first electric shaver for women was made

1941 Clothing coupons were introduced

Nylon was available in Britain, but in very short supply

The first aerosol went on sale in the US

1942 Fuel shortage brought fuel rationing, and driving for pleasure was prohibited

The Beveridge Report laid the foundations of the welfare state

The first sell-by date appeared, on Lyons Coffee

1944 The school leaving age was raised to 16, and PAYE tax was introduced

The first prefab went on show

1945 The end of the Second World War

The first atomic bombs were dropped on Japan

Fluorescent light arrived in Britain

In the US, Tupperware was launched and the first microwave was developed

1946 The government announced a plan to spend £380 million on new towns, to house 1 million people

Nylons were manufactured in the UK for the first time

Instant mashed potato was born

TV licences were issued

Tide was the first detergent specifically for clothes

1947 The government's nationalisation programme began with the coal mines

The Kenwood Chef was developed

1948 The Welfare State was established

The transistor was invented, eventually replacing the valve in TV and radio

The first plastic washing-up bowl was made

1949 The introduction of 7-inch records signalled the end for old 78s

The first British launderette was opened

Clothes rationing ended – but food rationing continued

work with running the home, many women worked harder than ever before. Basic everyday products were scarce: women became expert improvisers, using beetroot juice instead of lipstick and soot in the absence of eye shadow. The only new furniture available was government-controlled Utility furniture, and even that was in short supply.

A 1944 message from the Ministry of Fuel and Power

But if technological progress was static, family life itself changed dramatically. Many homes were suddenly without a man at their head, while women, even married women with children, had to go out to work. From 1943 all women aged between 18 and 45 were called on to work part-time – and as a result, reports showed that women's pay had risen by 80 per cent since the start of the war. This gave many women a taste of freedom which they

n the 1940s, making fridges, cookers and washing machines took second place to building warships

were reluctant to relinquish, even if there was nothing to spend their wages on. Also, reversing the inter-war trend towards isolated family units, people were now encouraged to live communally again, eating together to save fuel and food, and spending nights squeezed cheek by jowl with other families in air-raid shelters. The wireless had never been relied on more heavily, as families gathered round it for news of the war, and for light relief from the scrimping and the fear of daily life.

Good Housekeeping *at War*

Good Housekeeping's wartime role changed, too. Its concern was still household management, but now the Institute, instead of testing appliances, was helping housewives to get by with less and cope with rationing. The magazine, printed in a smaller format throughout the 1940s because of paper shortages, was packed with

Examples of 'home-made' furniture shown in our pages over past months are now on exhibition in our Furnishing Studio, 30 Grosvenor Gardens, London, S.W.1. Visitors are welcome, 9.30 to 5 p.m. Mondays to Fridays

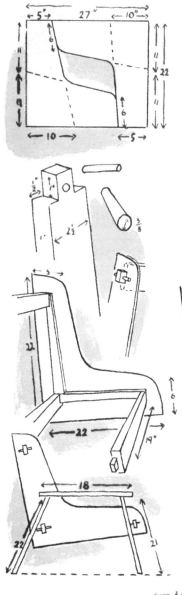

THE problem is easier if you try your hand at making some temporary furniture yourself, or enlist the aid of a local carpenter. Also, get rid of the idea that sprung upholstery is essential. In Sweden and America webbing is extensively used. It has spring, and is easy to fix.

This home-made chair is simple, strong and yet light enough to lift with one hand. The essential feature is the use of ¼-in. plywood for the sides. The amount needed is so small that you should have no trouble in getting an odd piece. For the seat and back, use heavy-quality webbing, which can be dyed.

The low table next to the chair has a drum-shaped base made of lino. Most

There are now **2,750,000** applications for utility furniture, and retailers cannot fill the orders.

New applications are being made at the rate of **12,000** a week, which is the maximum the Board of Trade can deal with.

MAKE IT YOUR SE

dealers have left-overs of a yard or two, for sale docket-free. The round top is of plywood, with the edges thickened by strips of wood, and involves some hard work with saw and sandpaper. However, a square top is equally good, and can easily be made from almost any wood, such as the end of a packing-case.

The diagrams on this page show the construction; further details are given opposite.

Send your furnishing queries to the Director of Good Housekeeping Furnishing Studio, at 30 Grosvenor Gardens, London, S.W.1. Please enclose a stamped addressed envelope

WEBBED can be cut about 27 b the square, continue rou a keyhole corners are paper. The shown in th ⅞ in. wood arms. The form tenons plywood sid then squari ends of the ⅜-in. bit, a rod (obtain hammered i and are gl and 1¼-in. s glue down t well in an strips of wo webbing of

SMALL Lino made and can fo Use a heav

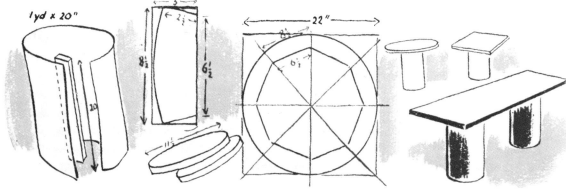

**Good
Housekeeping**
*encouraged its
readers to
'make do and
mend'*

damp-proof. A yard length forms a cylinder of convenient size. To make this take a strip of wood 2 or 3 in. wide, and a little shorter than the drum, to allow for inserting the top and bottom, and slightly shave off the edges of one side. Glue liberally, lay down one edge of your lino along centre line and tack. Then bend the lino round till the two edges meet, and tack. Use a block of wood inside the cylinder to hammer against. Wood discs $\frac{1}{2}$ in. or more thick are now glued and nailed into each end. To make these, saw a square round your circle, take off the corners to form an octagon, saw off corners again, and sandpaper.

Cut a circular top in the same fashion and fix to the drum with glue, or screw it to the upper disc before this is fixed in the lino. The plywood can be reinforced at the edge by eight pieces of wood cut to shape as the diagram. This is complicated, but very good practice! If your top is a nice piece of wood, give it a wax finish and paint the base to harmonise with your colour scheme. Two taller lino drums will obviously support a larger table, if you have a suitable top available. When proficient at sawing circles, try making the table lamp. Bore a hole in the centre of your wood base, which is about eight inches in diameter, and with a keyhole saw cut out a centre hole. A cardboard postal tube plugged with wood at the top to carry the electric fitting is inserted. Another method is to use a piece of broomstick. A groove in the side carries the flex, concealed by the decorative binding of window-cord shown in the illustration.

HAIR The two sides
piece of $\frac{1}{4}$-in. plywood
aw from the outside of
the inner angles. To
hers use a fretsaw or buy
your ironmonger. The
nd rounded with sand-
e construction is clearly
. Use $2\frac{1}{2}$ in. by 1 in. or
ee cross-pieces, legs and
e cross-pieces are cut to
into square holes in the
re made by boring and
ning with a chisel. The
s are then bored with a
egs cut from $\frac{3}{8}$-in. dowel
most ironmongers) are
joints should fit tightly,
ttach the legs, use glue
or five to each leg. Now
ces and punch long nails
th plastic wood. Glue
sides, to hold the cross-
d back.

ND ELECTRIC LAMP :
m is surprisingly strong
for a variety of tables.
preferably 'backed' or

Good Housekeeping
OCTOBER
Vol. XLIV   No. 4

*"Good Housekeeping" Editorial
Offices, Good Housekeeping Institute,
Good Housekeeping Centre, and Good
Housekeeping School of Cookery :* 28-
30 Grosvenor Gardens, London, S.W.1.
*The Editor will not hold himself
responsible for the safety of any MSS.,
but when stamps are enclosed he will
make every effort to ensure their safe
return.*
*The Editor begs to inform the readers
of GOOD HOUSEKEEPING that
the characters in the stories in this
number are purely imaginary, and that
no reference or allusion is intended to
apply to any living person or persons.*

What do You Think
Part-time Principle?

RECENTLY, enquiring of one of our senior colleagues how his wife managed with her part-time factory work, we were told "She likes it—though she thought she wouldn't." Pursuing the subject, it transpired that the lady was not so much enamoured of assembling nuts at the bench, but that she enjoyed the extraordinary variety of human contacts and getting away from the house, where incidentally she does a full-size job in raising live-stock and garden produce, as well as running the home.

We found this specially interesting, as it dovetailed very nicely with a theory we've been turning over in our minds. The theory is briefly that the "part-time principle" is one of the good things that has come out of the war; too good, in fact, to be lost when peace comes.

You may remember that when the demand for labour first became acute and it was suggested that factories, and shops and offices, too, should try a short-shift system so that house-wives could work part-time, the great mass of employers obstinately set their faces against it. Later, pressure of events made them think again. After the preliminary organisation was done, they found to their surprise that not only did the part-time system work well, but it increased output, as the amount of work done per hour over a short shift was substantially more than when full hours were worked.

In this last sentence lies the whole core of the matter. If short working hours mean more output per hour, as they can and do if workers go "all out" while they are at it, cannot we reorganise our whole system so that everyone puts in less hours at his main job, and so has time and energy for taking on some contrasting part-time occupation?

How would this work out? Let's take the case of the house-wife. With better housing and improved domestic appliances, household work could be speeded up, though not perhaps in all cases, quite enough to free her for outside part-time work, paid or voluntary. However, to even things out, the house-wife would rely on the part-time work in the home put in by her husband, whose shorter main-job working hours would leave him sufficient time and energy for it. Thus, while the wife would enjoy outside contacts and the stimulus of a different kind of work, whether it might be serving on the local Council, or selling hats in the local store, helping in a Nursery School or in one of the new Continuation Schools, the husband would be able to spend more time in enjoying and taking an active part in the upbringing of his children, in exercising his creative skill at the kitchen stove or in putting down for winter the fruits of his husbandry in the garden. Isn't there the basis of a truer and therefore happier married partnership here, than when the wife gets housebound and circumscribed in outlook, and the husband comes home from long hours outside the home to relax like an oriental pasha, while wondering what has happened that his wife has grown so dull?

This 1943 editorial shows how the war changed attitudes to women and work

Now *that* Soap *is* Rationed

**By
P. L. GARBUTT**
Director of Good
Housekeeping Institute

This is the soap allowance for a family of four, apportioned equally between soap flakes, laundry soap, No. 1 soap powder, and toilet soap

Small wonder that there are always laundry problems in the Institute mail, now that soap is rationed and laundries often will not accept new customers. It is not easy to make the soap last out, especially where there are children, but you can help yourself quite a lot by taking a little trouble.

Here are some of the questions we have been asked recently, and among them may be your problem, too. If not, write and let us know your difficulty.

Query I : Soap Rationing

The first question comes from the mother of a family who is anxious to know how she can best soften water and so save her soap ration. This question is published because it is a difficulty shared to some extent by all readers just now.

Our Advice

(1) Install a mains softener if, like our questioner, you live in a hard-water district, are able to secure a model, and can meet the cost. (We ascertained, by the way, that models were available at the time of writing.)

(2) Alternatively, collect and use rain-water for washing and household cleaning purposes, if possible.

(3) If, for one reason or another, the above suggestions are impracticable, use soda to soften the water, but be *very* careful not to use too much, especially when washing delicate articles. Actually, *very little* indeed is required, far less than most people imagine.

The simplest and safest way of using washing soda is to dissolve 1 oz. in a pint of water and bottle this solution, adding about 1 tablespoonful to every gallon of hot water for every 5 degrees of hardness, i.e., for water of 20 degrees of hardness, add 4 tablespoonfuls per gallon. (Your water company will tell

you the degree of hardness of your water supply.) Place requisite quantity of soda solution in a bowl before running in the hot water, and leave for a moment or two, if possible, so that it has a chance of reacting with the hardness before you add the soap. This may sound a little complicated, but is actually very simple once you have ascertained the hardness of your water and measured up the bowl or bath you generally use. Adding the required amount of soda *before* the soap will, indeed, soon become a habit, and a very worthwhile one, which may save you a really big proportion of your soap ration, possibly as much as a quarter.

Query II : Washing Woollens

"After using lukewarm water for years, I have been told that woollens can be washed successfully with boiling water. I should like to have your opinion."

Our Advice

We explained to our reader that there are several satisfactory ways of washing woollens, and that one involves the use of practically boiling water. This method gives very good results, provided care is taken not to immerse the wool in cold water immediately after the hot. If, however,

articles are left in the washing water until cool enough to handle, and rinsing water of about the same temperature is used, no harm will result. Many people prefer to wash woollens in this way rather than in the more usually accepted one, involving the use of water at about blood heat.

Things to avoid when washing woollens are : (1) rubbing, which very soon causes felting and shrinkage; (2) extremes of temperature; (3) the use of strong alkalies, such as soda, all of which are injurious.

Query III : Substitutes for Laundry Starch

"Can you tell me of any satisfactory substitute for laundry starch, which is now unprocurable in my district?"

Our Advice

We explained that satisfactory substitutes for laundry starch are farinaceous substances, such as flour, rice-water, etc., all of which are valuable foodstuffs and should, therefore, not be used for other than feeding purposes in war-time. For thin muslin articles gum arabic is sometimes used, but this only gives very slight stiffening, and may not be easy to obtain at the present time. In any case, it is unsuitable for heavy articles.

Good Housekeeping *in a more practical mood in 1942*

THE TOWN OF THE FUTURE

■ There can be no doubt that our future towns will be as different from those we knew before the war as a radiogram is different from our first crystal set. And just as our admiration for the elegance and the greater efficiency of the modern does not in any way impair our affection for the old-fashioned, so we need have no regrets when we come to live in the town of the future.

Towns and cities damaged by the war are already considering their rebuilding plans. Residential districts, we are told, will be designed on the garden city principle of villas or semi-detached houses each with its own garden; or ten-storey blocks of flats surrounded by communal lawns, flower walks and rose arbours. It is gratifying to note that experts are planning for a 'green and pleasant land' with plenty of space, light and fresh air. In the past, towns and cities have straggled and sprawled, capturing parts of the countryside with the same inevitable disappointment as the caging of a wild bird. The town of the future will be erect and compact, with the trees, the grass and the flowers of the country-side brought to its front doors. Schools and playgrounds for the children will be included as an integral part of the communal plan. These will be so positioned that children will not have to cross main roads on their way to school. The Shopping Centre, in view of its supreme importance to housewives, will receive very special attention. Architects, remembering the British climate, will develop the arcade principle for greater all-the-year-round convenience, specially appreciated on wet shopping days.

Ancient buildings will be restored and records and relics of a glorious past preserved. The town of the future will retain its cherished character, its unique individuality and its historical associations, yet it will sparkle and shine in its new pride.

New buildings, new services, new homes, rising up from the ruins of the old, will make for happier family life in Britain after the war. The better environment will invite us to make the most of our longer leisure and will encourage us to seek new interests within the pleasant, comfortable and healthy precincts of our new homes.

Pears

RENOWNED AS THE LEADING TOILET SOAP SINCE 1789

TP/242/34   *No. 4 of a series of advertisements issued by A. & F. Pears, Ltd., Isleworth, Middlesex.*

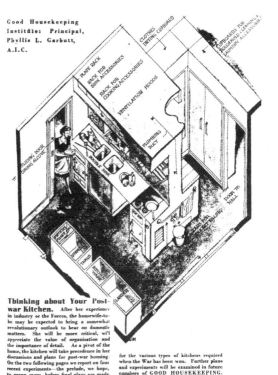

Good Housekeeping
Institute: Principal,
Phyllis L. Garbutt,
A.I.C.

Thinking about Your Post-war Kitchen. After her experience in industry or the Forces, the housewife-to-be may be expected to bring a somewhat revolutionary outlook to bear on domestic matters. She will be more critical, wi'l appreciate the value of organisation and the importance of detail. As a pivot of the home, the kitchen will take precedence in her discussions and plans for post-war housing. On the two following pages we report on four recent experiments—the prelude, we hope, to many more, before final plans are made for the various types of kitchens required when the War has been won. Further plans and experiments will be examined in future numbers of GOOD HOUSEKEEPING.

Above and overleaf: Looking forward to sophisticated post-war kitchens

energy-saving ideas, nutritious recipes and patriotic articles, plus a dollop of escapism thrown in, in the form of fiction and humorous articles.

Advertising was also drastically reduced in the war years, because there were so few goods to sell. Companies who continued to advertise often did so in the form of apologies to consumers for the lack of goods available, or even with exhortations to use less of their products – a concept that's hard to imagine today. Towards the end of the war, advertisers, the government and *Good Housekeeping* itself were united in the theme of 'jam tomorrow', giving reassurances that life would be wonderful when peace came. In the days of austerity, housewives could at least dream of a future filled with appliances and consumer goods that were bigger and better than before. Pears (opposite) took out a series of adverts predicting (presciently) that life after the war would consist of high-rise flats, shopping centres and foreign holidays; while *Good Housekeeping* promised in 1944, 'Great expectations – and opportunities – lie ahead. Women's views, and women's needs in their homes, are being considered more today than they have ever been before. The post-war kitchen is being discussed everywhere.' Everyone believed that better times were just around the corner.

Waiting for a Brave New World

However, this was far from the truth. Britain's post-war financial crisis – the result of massive wartime spending – meant that even after the manufacture of appliances restarted, most were earmarked for export. In 1949 Prestcold refrigerators advertised, 'Let's face it…we know you're disappointed. We too had hoped you'd have one of the fine, post-war Prestcold Refrigerators by now, for we're making

*Above, generous floor-to-ceiling storage space makes this kitchen a joy
to the methodical housewife. All the working surfaces are at one level*

*A heat-storage cooker of sturdy modern design is the feature of the
kitchen shown above. Note the recessed metal rack for pans, the
double sink with its "mixer" tap, and the cornerless work-table*

*Right, an example of a converted country kitchen showing another
modern solid-fuel cooker. Draining-board space is generous,
so are the airing-rail and the storage shelf for saucepans*

MANCHESTER

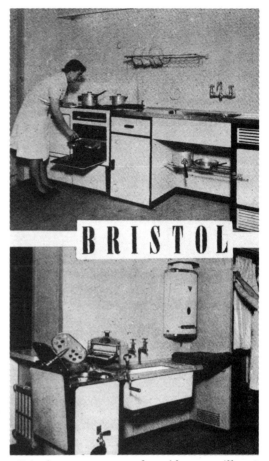

BRISTOL

Cooker and boiler in this kitchen are placed in a canopied recess which carries away cooking smells

Your 1946 Kitchen?

IN these pictures you are sure to find some features, at least, that you would like included in your own post-war kitchen. Send us your comments, criticisms, ideas. For the best 500-word essay on " My 1946 Kitchen," GOOD HOUSEKEEPING offers :

First prize—Defence Bond Unit for £10.
Second prize— ,, ,, ,, ,, £5.
Three prizes—One Savings Certificate each.

Please write clearly in ink, and address your entries to " Kitchen," Good Housekeeping Institute, 30 Grosvenor Gardens, London, S.W.1. Closing date, by which all entries must be received, March 31st.

Bristol suggests a gas cooker with oven grill and a U-shaped kitchen with separate laundry section

Guildford's " stable " door is popular ; so is the vegetable rack built in under the refrigerator

KENT

GUILDFORD

COLD FACTS ABOUT

PRESTCOLD
Refrigerators

◆

LET'S FACE IT....

We know you're disappointed. We too had hoped you'd have one of the fine, post-war Prestcold Refrigerators by now, for we're making them in their thousands. You would have, too, but for export.

WHAT ABOUT
MY KITCHEN?

"Export, Export!" you say. "Must *all* good things in Britain go abroad?" The answer is yes—and no. The great majority must. And among them are of course Prestcold Refrigerators. But there are a *few* for home needs.

" They get a warm welcome overseas !"

WHO MAKES THEM?

Prestcold Refrigerators are made by Britain's largest manufacturers of automatic refrigeration. Among the 8000 workpeople at the great Cowley factory are skilled designers, engineers, technicians, craftsmen, whose pride is to build Britain's finest refrigeration equipment — domestic, commercial, industrial, scientific. Try *hard* to get one for yourself. Numbers *are* increasing—see your dealer.

"We get so used to this business of grumbling"

"T HAT'S two buses we've missed," said the lady in brown. " Full up, indeed — well, I'm *fed* up! Fed up with waiting for everything!"

" But, dear — you've just got that electric kettle you've been waiting for, and the people at the Electricity Showrooms have just told you . . ."

" Of course " — the lady in brown brightened up — " we get so used to grumbling about this business of having to be patient, we forget that things *are* picking up a bit."

" Yes! I waited for my husband to be demobbed, and he's back! We waited for our house to be repaired. It's done! And now we're waiting, like you, for it to be brought *really* up to date — we're making it an *electric* home."

" Pity more people don't call on the Electricity Showrooms and find out about the things they'll soon have for us — airing cupboards, washers and water-heaters and all that."

" Electricity is truly a wonderful and well-organised thing: I sometimes wonder whether we *should* take it so much for granted . . ."

Electricity...
Wonderful thing!

Above and overleaf: manufacturers of everything from nylons to refrigerators apologised
for shortages and made promises for the future

them in their thousands. You would have, too, but for export.'

World food shortages combined with severe financial problems meant that stringent rationing continued, and the brave new world failed to materialise. By the end of the 1940s women who had spent ten years scrimping, saving fuel and living on rationed food were becoming extremely disillusioned. Despite a post-war baby boom, there was also a huge rise in divorce, revealing how much the war had disrupted family life. In 1947 there were 60,000 divorces – ten times the pre-war annual figure.

However, while it probably didn't feel like it at the time, the late 1940s was a hugely important period, in which the foundations were being laid for the boom time of the 1950s. Although they didn't yet filter through to the average home, scientific developments made in the war – often called the physicists' war – led to the founding of the electronics and optics industries, as well as creating advances in aviation, communications and the manufacture of plastics and other man-made materials. Work on radio-waves led to the invention of the microwave oven, and the transistor transformed radios and televisions.

Building for the Future

In the 1946 New Town Act the government announced a massive scheme to build 3-4 million new homes, to replace those bombed during the war. A Ministry of Health report promised bigger houses, with three bedrooms, well-equipped kitchens, better heating, constant hot water and larger windows, and 'what has been the long-felt want of the average family: a clean, cheerful room where meals can be taken with the maximum of convenience to the housewife.' In the meantime, 'prefabs' were made as a stop gap – metal houses built by the motor trade to house demobbed servicemen and bombed-out families. In all, around 157,000 prefabs were constructed – and although they were supposed to be a temporary measure, some are still standing today. The electrification programme also continued – by 1948, 86 per cent of homes had electricity.

Nylons are coming!

We'll have Nylon stockings soon—isn't it marvellous news! Our guess is that you can hardly wait. And when you get your Nylons you'll certainly want to have Lux to look after them. You remember how safe and gentle Lux was? Remember how it could keep stockings and fine things like new? With Lux you didn't need to rub, and how easily it rinsed out! Don't ever forget how lovely Lux was, because it *will* be back. But nowadays, when you use the soaps or flakes available, do take extra care.

REPORTED BY THE **LUX** FASHION SCOUT

THE quaint looking G.E.C. electric heater of 1914 is linked with its modern stream-lined version by over a quarter of a century of continuous progress in the electrical industry. Science never stands still—not even in wartime—and just as the G.E.C. continued to progress through the last war, so to-day it is keeping abreast of the latest developments and improvements in everything electrical for the home.

Remember

FOR EVERYTHING ELECTRICAL

In 1941, GEC reflected on former glories

The government's ambitious plans for the reconstruction of Britain continued in 1948 when the Labour government established the welfare state, with free health care for all, pensions, and child allowance, and the promise of full-time education for all children up to the age of 16.

The other big hope for the future was television. Transmission began again after the war, and by 1948 60,000 homes had televisions, with a waiting list for new sets. A *Good Housekeeping* article, 'Television spreads its wings', told readers that with the opening in 1949 of Britain's first regional station in the Midlands, television would be within reach of a much larger number of viewers. 'People who "look in" at a television set today are not only sharing in a commendable present but helping to build a great future for the entertainment of millions in their homes.'

By the time the blitzed, battered, make-do-and-mend 1940s drew to a close, better times really were just around the corner.

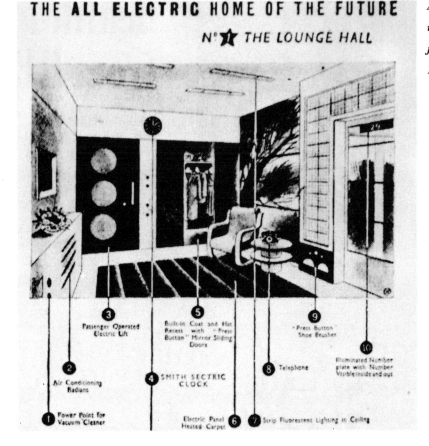

A high-tech vision of the future from 1944

In June 1941, *Good Housekeeping* helped housewives to plan their household routine. The plan shows the average housewife working a 14-hour day, even with the help of a charwoman.

The daily plan of work for a married woman at home with a baby while her husband was away in the Army, in a small three-bedroomed house with a charlady once a week:

daily plan of work

7.00 a.m. Rise, attend to boiler, grates, etc., and relight fire if necessary. Dress and attend to baby. **8 a.m**. Prepare breakfast. **8.15** Breakfast. **8.45** Clear away and wash up. **9.00** Sweep, dust and tidy living rooms. Make beds. Dust and tidy bedrooms. Attend to baby's washing. Undertake own personal laundrywork at this time on Mondays. Clean bathroom and lavatory. **11.30** Put baby to sleep. Sweep stairs and hall. Prepare dinner. **1.00 p.m**. Dinner. **1.30** Wash up dinner things. Sweep and tidy kitchen. Rest. **2.30-4.30** Take baby out. **5.0** Tea. **5.30** Clear away tea things and wash up. **6-6.30** Baby bathed and put to bed. **6.30-7.30** Ironing, when necessary. Clean silver one day weekly. Do mending.

charwoman's duties:

Every week: Morning: Clean front and back entrance. **Weekly** clean landing, stairs and hall. **Afternoon**: Weekly clean kitchen, bathroom and lavatory.

Alternate weeks: Morning: Weekly clean dining room and sitting room.

Afternoon: Weekly clean best and child's bedroom.

JUST AROUND THE CORNER

"Tala" REGD.

KITCHENWARE

—Yes, we hope the time is near when the present shortage will cease and "Tala" Kitchenware will again give kitchens that extra sparkle and that efficient service for which "Tala" articles are famed all over the world.

for Beauty and Efficiency

"LOOK! I'm all finished in the kitchen . . . when does the play start?"

Time to spare—thanks to VIM
because Vim is the speediest cleanser
8d per canister

V 156B-981-120   *Selling Agents: Hudson & Knight Limited*

The 1950s:
BOOM TIME

IN THE 1950S THE JAM ARRIVED. THE BETTER life promised in the 1940s became a reality for a huge proportion of the population and changes in the home and in family life were more dramatic and more widespread than any of those before the war. The standard of living for most people rose: they were earning more, living in better homes, and were warmer, better fed and better dressed. The technology which had been trickling into homes in the 1930s became a deluge, while the growth of television and TV advertising broadened horizons and raised expectations. Many of the appliances and products we take for granted today made their first appearance in the 1950s – from Squezy liquid (opposite), Mother's Pride sliced bread, plastic and Formica to stereo hi-fis, spin driers, supermarkets and steam irons.

Dream Homes

The decade started in optimistic mood with the Festival of Britain in 1951, held on a transformed bomb-site on London's South Bank. Its 'Dome of Discovery' heralded a brighter future; the emphasis was on colour, fun and fantasy, in stark contrast to the austere war years.

In 1951, a survey found that the average housewife worked a 75-hour week

SQEZY LIQUID
cheaper washing-up
one pack outlasts
two large packets of powder

just one squeeze
never a drop wasted

dishes done faster
dissolves grease in a flash
. . . dries with a shine

hands soft and smooth
contains GLYCERINE

Easier, faster, cheaper dishwashing
. . . . that's Sqezy, the miracle
quick washing-up liquid. No
measuring or shaking . . . just pick
up and squeeze. *Hey presto*, lots
of energy-packed suds dissolve
grease in a flash, leaving dishes
sparkling bright. *No need to rinse
or wipe*, dishes shine as they dry.
Get Sqezy today.

ONLY
2/-
LASTS FOR
WEEKS

It's easy with SQEZY
in the easy *squeezy* pack

Domestos Ltd., Newcastle upon Tyne.

One of the biggest crowd-pullers was 'the Home of the Future', featuring uncluttered rooms, electrical appliances galore and the new ideal for the 1950s housewife – a fitted kitchen. In the same year a Mass Observation study found that the average British housewife worked a 75-hour week – spending about a quarter of her time in the kitchen. It wasn't surprising that women were crying out for new kitchens and more labour-saving gadgets.

The whole population was by now desperate for an end to scarcity and scrimping, and for the chance to buy the goods they'd been reading about for so long, and circumstances combined to make this possible. In 1953 Chancellor Rab Butler announced a 'new look' budget, reducing income tax and purchase tax. Employment, in the huge government building projects, and in the booming manufacturing industries, was in plentiful supply, giving unprecedented spending power. And at last there was plenty to buy. Rationing ended completely in 1954 and the export drive was over: suddenly those longed-for goods were widely available and mass-production techniques made them more affordable than ever before. If they couldn't be bought outright, hire purchase was popular.

the booming fifties

1951   The Festival of Britain

The first smokeless zone was introduced, in Coventry

Premier became Britain's first supermarket chain

Diners' Club was the first credit card in the UK

Terylene garments were manufactured

1952   The British Standards Institute Kite Mark was introduced

Tetleys made the first teabags

The telephone answering machine was invented

1953   The coronation of Queen Elizabeth II

1954   All rationing finally ended

IBM launched an 'electronic brain' – a forerunner of the computer

Russell and Hobbs developed the first automatic electric kettle

The first edition of Yellow Pages came out.

1955   ITV made its first broadcast – and its first advert, for toothpaste

Wimpy opened Britain's first hamburger chain

The first fish fingers went on sale

1956   The Suez crisis

The first Teflon-coated non-stick frying pans were made in America

1957   Combined washer/spin driers appeared in launderettes

The first microwave oven came to Britain

1958   Stereo 'hi-fi' equipment and discs were launched

The first domestic tumble drier was produced

1959   The first mini radios using transistors went on sale

The invention of Velcro, the cassette tape, and the birth of Barbie dolls all took place

The first stretch of the M1 motorway was opened

The dream home became a possibility for millions as the new towns promised in 1946 began to materialise – towns such as Stevenage, Harlow, Corby and Peterlee. Houses and flats were being built at a rate of around 300,000 a year, and by 1958 10 million people lived in post-war homes, many of them privately owned thanks to more accessible mortgages. The houses were relatively large, had electricity, gas, bathrooms, gardens, and sometimes central heating, and at their heart the fitted kitchen, with Formica units and space for a host of appliances.

Plastic Perfection

The era of the neat, colour-coordinated kitchen with built-in units was made possible by the development of tough laminated plastics, the most popular being Formica, used for worktops, tables and cupboards. Formica had been invented in 1913, but only now was it mass-produced in a range of colours and patterns, giving the 1950s kitchen its distinctive look. Wipe-clean surfaces meant an end to scrubbing and scouring; while stainless-steel sinks replaced the old chip-prone enamel. Lighter polythene-based plastic also transformed the kitchen, appearing in the form of washing-up bowls, bins, laundry baskets, storage jars,

Cooking's more fun in a gay kitchen

See how 'Alkathene' Houseware brightens things up!

BRIGHT COLOURS make a lot of difference to your home, to your mood, and to *you*! Gay, lovely kitchen things made from 'Alkathene' make cooking more attractive, less like hard work. 'Alkathene' is long-lasting, hygienic, virtually unbreakable. It will not chip or dent or scratch. It can be washed clean in a jiffy with soap and water. It is as light as a feather. 'Alkathene' household goods come in a wide range of cheerful colours, made by many manufacturers. Whichever brand you choose, look for the label that says Made From 'Alkathene'.

LOOK FOR THIS LABEL.

MADE FROM 'ALKATHENE'

It's light! It's bright! 'ALKATHENE'

IT'S MADE FROM

IMPERIAL CHEMICAL INDUSTRIES LIMITED · LONDON · S.W.1

Look at Mummy's Washing doing itself!

It's child's-play with a BENDIX. All you have to do is put in the soiled clothes, set the dials and add the soap. BENDIX *automatically* SOAKS . . . WASHES . . . RINSES THREE TIMES . . . DRAINS . . . DAMP DRIES . . . SWITCHES ITSELF OFF . . .

BENDIX *automatically* THE BEST!

BENDIX HOME APPLIANCES LTD. (Dept. J) · ALBION WORKS · KINGSBURY ROAD · BIRMINGHAM 24

it's a great *New* combination!

Servis
AUTOMATIC DRYER
Supertwin
for home laundry economy

giving you . . . TANGLE-FREE WASHING and EXCLUSIVE "DEEP RINSE" . . . . "SPIN-DRYING"!!

Quick wash, spin and spin-rinse cycle deals with a large load in a few moments! Backed by 'Servis'

Send for full colour leaflet of the SERVIS 'SUPERTWIN'

SERVIS DOMESTIC APPLIANCES · DARLASTON · SOUTH STAFFS.

THE ▮LOOK▮ IN A WOMAN'S EYES...

' What a lovely cooker ' say the eyes 'modern and practical, high grill, boiling burners that light by magic, big oven, storage drawer, colour . . . and most of all look at the styling! Imagine the look on our friends' faces when they see our RENOWN Six.'

The RENOWN Six with the

PARKINSON COWAN look

You will see it at your GAS SHOWROOMS—and be surprised that the Renown Six costs only £49 19s 6d.

Best of the Gas Cookers

PARKINSON COWAN APPLIANCES LIMITED BIRMINGHAM

Adverts showed the model housewife, happy and fulfilled in her push-button kitchen

tablecloths – its uses were endless, and every month the pages of *Good Housekeeping* seemed to feature it in a new guise. New oil-based detergents and washing-up liquids such as Squezy and Fairy, in easy-to-use plastic bottles, made lighter work of cleaning, while man-made fibres such as Terylene and nylon, developed in the 1940s, began to be used in clothing, promising to make washing and drying easier.

The dream kitchen was well stocked with appliances. Spending on electrical goods in the 1950s was six times higher than any other consumer spending, and ownership of washing machines and vacuum cleaners doubled. The new white goods were more streamlined and sophisticated than their pre-war cousins. The introduction of the spin drier brought the twin-tub washing machine – earlier models had still relied on a wringer to dry clothes – and the first front-loading washers became available, although these didn't yet have a spin drier combined. Later in the decade adverts start to appear in *Good Housekeeping* for tumble-driers, but these were expensive to buy and run, and were slow to become popular.

Gas and electric cookers continued to jostle for supremacy. By 1961 30 per cent of homes cooked electric, and both types of cooker became more sophisticated, with standardised thermostats, high-level grills, clear glass doors, automatic ignition and timers.

Fridges became more of a necessity than a luxury as houses were built without cool larders, and central heating made storage more difficult in winter: in 1953 only 3.5 per cent of homes had a fridge, but by 1965 the figure was 56 per cent. Post-war fridges usually had a freezer compartment, and domestic chest freezers arrived in the middle of the decade, leading to a market for the frozen food industry. Dishwashers too improved, but were still expensive and failed to make a major impact.

The 1950s manufacturing boom also brought a rash of smaller appliances: heated hostess trolleys, teasmades, heated rollers, new steam irons and heated trays. Russell and Hobbs developed both the automatic kettle (below) and the coffee percolator, while the Kenwood Chef was one of the most popular mixers, with attachments for mincing, slicing, juicing, chopping and blending. One side-effect of this mechanisation of the kitchen was that it became a more acceptable place for men to be: although housework was still predominantly women's work, it was no longer unheard of for a man to cook a meal, or at least lend a hand, as Johnny did to Fanny Craddock in their TV kitchen

The Rise of Television

While women's domestic lives were becoming dominated by gadgetry, another invention was changing family life. After its slow beginnings, television took the country by storm – in 1950 344,000 homes owned a television; in 1951 alone a further 250,000 were produced. Prices were dropping, and the network widening – by 1952 four out of five homes could

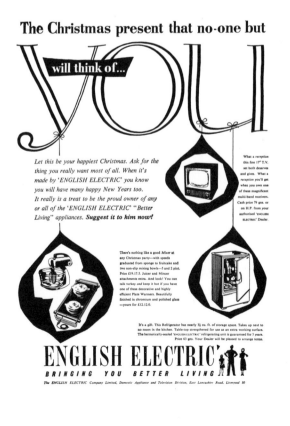

Ads for new electrical gadgets filled the pages of Good Housekeeping in the 1950s

receive TV signals. The television broadcast of the Coronation in 1953 boosted sales and by 1961 75 per cent of families had a set, with the average viewer watching 12½ hours a week. The launch of ITV in 1955 brought advertising directly into the living room: television was the perfect medium for selling everything from toothpaste to washing machines to a captive audience.

When 1950s families weren't glued to the television, many were out in the car. Ownership rose from just over 2 million in 1950 to 5½ million in 1960 (though still very low compared with today), and the car's popularity forced the construction of the first motorways – followed almost immediately by traffic jams. Reading women's magazines was another popular leisure pursuit. New magazines abounded; and total advertising revenue increased from £1.1 million in 1951 to £5.3 million in 1958.

Mother's Little Helpers

Given the scale of the 1950s consumer boom, it's not surprising that in 1957 Harold Macmillan felt able to claim that the British had 'never had it so good'. Certainly, this seemed to be true for the 1950s housewife who, in her wipe-clean, mechanised home, did far less hard physical labour than her mother's generation. Yet in new towns and suburbs around Britain the pre-war bogey, 'suburban neurosis', was reappearing. After experiencing the independence of the war years, women found themselves imprisoned in the kitchen once more. Many women were lonely in the new towns, and expectations of them were high. Housewifely skills were lauded; entertaining was popular and books, magazines and television programmes idealised the perfect hostess, attractively turned out in her pretty frilled apron, whipping up gourmet meals in minutes in the style of the new TV cooks, keeping a sparkling home and raising perfect children. Appliances might have made housework less physically demanding, but it was still mechanical and repetitive work, and another Mass Observation survey in 1957 showed little overall reduction in the amount of time spent doing it. This was also the time when keeping up with the Joneses started to matter, and the desire to be part of the consumer boom was another source of pressure. In the late 1950s doctors began to voice concerns about the number of housewives taking tranquillisers, 'mother's little helpers', to help with depression. Divorce rates also continued to rise. Dream homes and kitchens did not necessarily bring dream lives.

One solution to boredom and isolation was to work outside the home, and the rise of the working mother began in the 1950s. Four million married women were in paid employment in 1958, compared with two million ten years earlier – but even that was a drop in the ocean compared with what was to come.

STARTING FROM SCRATCH

Mainly for brides, who want to know about the brand-new way to keep house

Once upon a time a girl learned the art of good housekeeping at her mother's knee, or at her elbow at any rate. She married and ran her home as she had been taught and made a very good job of it. You, we hope, have not grown up " hardly able to boil an egg," but, to be honest, does the prospect of making as good a job of housekeeping as you have done of your career seem a bit remote? And you want to keep on your job, at least until you start a family? Then it is even more important to know about new products, about new ideas that help to lighten a housewife's load. Mothers, grandmothers, aunts and the rest, when they want to adopt new ideas are often fettered by old but still good equipment. You, on the other hand, are starting from scratch, and there is no real reason why you should not start with the newest. Not, mind you, because it is the newest, but because it is likely to be the best. Designers and scientists are working every day on new lines and improving the old ones. Accept that housekeeping, like everything else, is deep in the machine age, but acknowledge, too, that the mechanical side is not the end of the story. Some of the old ways, the old tools, have never been bettered, it is true, but new materials also come into the picture. Never dismiss the wonders of the age as " only plastic." Know that silicones, for instance, are easier to use than elbow grease. So here we list, for any bride or bride-to-be, a selection of what is good and up-to-date in home-making equipment. Some of it is expensive, but not all of it, and the smallest useful tool can become treasure in her kitchen.

No bending down or wringing out with this Prestige Minit mop— it has its own squeegee on the handle. With it she is using a plastic bucket from Bex. She chose it in pale green and teamed it with other matching kitchen ware

For prices and stockists, see page 202

109

A 1955 guide for newly-weds setting up home

STARTING FROM SCRATCH

Entertaining, for instance,

is bliss for a bride in

her very first home—even

when she is out all day ....

because she chose an **English Electric** automatic cooker which cooks the meal while she is out, and turns itself off when it is done . . . and a new **Tempo** kettle to boil in next to no time.   Then she found a **Moka Express** coffee-maker for the fun, ease and flavour, of espresso coffee, and added a **Morphy-Richards** toaster because all she has to do is cut the bread and put it in; the toaster does the rest

She doesn't have to search for uncrumpled doilies.   She chooses plastic, dainty as lace; uses them again and again and again

Nor does she scurry in and out of the kitchen wondering if the next course is still all right.   She has a very handsome hot plate

A very smart gift, this one—a Rotel mixer from Switzerland which does literally everything but clean the food and cook it and is more than ordinarily safe and simple to use

←

A spoon with holes in it for straining and a serrated edge for cutting is fine for serving cooked fruit and vegetables

↓

If our girl was buying her own machine she could start with this juice extractor and add the rest later ↑

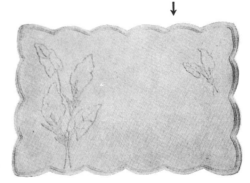

Plastic again, this time to ease the laundry bills and ensure that there is always a clean tray-cloth

↓

If she wants a little mixer, something quick and handy to mix a cake for tea or whip the cream stiff in a minute or two, here is the Kenwood Minor

→

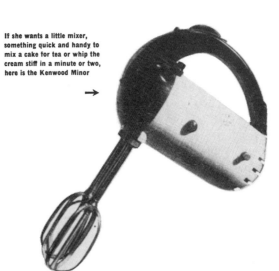

For prices and stockists, see page 202

The 1960s:

THE WHITE HEAT OF TECHNOLOGY

IN MARCH 1962, *GOOD HOUSEKEEPING* celebrated its 40th birthday by looking back over

the remarkable developments of the preceding decades, and by making some

predictions for the future:

> 'In forty years time one thing is certain: there will be far more leisure for everyone
>
> and less drudgery... we are replacing the housewife's muscles by electric motors
>
> and her brain power by automation.'

This was typical of the optimism of the time. The feeling in the early 1960s was that

the new affluence and rising standards of living of the 1950s were now the norm.

Wartime austerity was long forgotten, replaced by confidence that life was getting

better all the time. Harold Wilson boasted of a country fuelled by 'the white heat of

technological revolution'. High-rise flats transformed rundown inner cities such as

Birmingham, Newcastle and Glasgow, and wages were high-rise too – 1961's

average weekly wage of around £15 grew to £28 by the end of the decade,

financing consumerism in the home on a scale that left even the booming 1950s

behind.

Inflation was on the increase too, but the cost of many household

the affluent sixties

1960 National Service was ended

Plastic carrier bags and refuse sacks were used for the first time

Miele introduced the first automatic dishwasher

1961 The first contraceptive pill became generally available

Russian Yuri Gagarin was the first man in space

The electric toothbrush and fruit yogurt were introduced to the UK

1962 The first transatlantic television broadcasts with US satellites were made

Aluminium foil and flavoured crisps reached Britain

1963 The Beatles recorded their first LP

President Kennedy was assassinated

Valium was developed in the US

1964 Beeching's mass closure of railway lines was announced.

A 20-year plan was announced to build more new towns – including Milton Keynes

BBC2 went on air and the first portable TV was launched, with an 11-inch screen.

In the USA, IBM developed the first word processor

1965 The death penalty was abolished in the UK

Mary Whitehouse set up the National Viewers' and Listeners' Association

1966 Barclays Bank introduced Barclaycard, the first British credit card

The conversion to natural gas began

The first push-button phones appeared

1967 The first colour television transmission by the BBC was made

Barclays introduced the first cash-dispensing machine in the UK

The first heart transplant took place

The first quartz watch went on sale

1968 The Creda self-cleaning oven went on sale

1969 Concorde made its maiden flight

High-grade oil was discovered in the North Sea

The microprocessor was developed

LIVING ELECTRICALLY IN

1960

Health and happiness for the whole family

Easy to work, efficient in perform-ance, enjoyable to use—just three aspects of electric gadgets and machines today. And the results of increasing automation? Time saved, wider scope for leisure hobbies, greater cleanliness, more safeguards to health—and pride in a job well done. All this is not just the good fortune of the housewife; the benefits are reaped by the whole family, young or old, married or single, working or retired, in the home and out of it. All the time new ideas are being perfected, developments carried out, possibilities explored, and in this, our annual Living Electrically feature, amid the multiplic-ity of appliances, we have chosen just a few which affect the mode of life of the family, transforming work into pleasure and mere comfort into luxurious living.

● A family undoubt-edly makes a lot of work and, to cope with this, family-size appli-ances are more and more in demand, in-corporating the latest innovations and lab-our-saving gadgets.

Take catering, for instance: no longer need a bare larder greet the unexpected guest, or a glut of fruit be wasted, if the family has a refriger-ator equipped with an extra low temperature freezer section for frozen food storage and for quick-freezing home produce—and defrosting is usually fully automatic.

Now consider the modern family kitchen: built-in cooker units with hobs separately sited, handy to a working surface, can even allow two people to use the rings at the same time. The oven, too, is a separate unit, and built at the right height to avoid stooping. There may

Electrolux, model 65, £29 11s. 5d.

GH—12*

be a spit built into the oven, an automatic roasting meter and oven shelves that move to the required height at the turn of a knob, as additional luxury items.

A WAY WITH THE WASH

Washday in flat or farmhouse—every family's needs are catered for with a wide range of washing-machines and driers, or combination models which receive the clothes dirty and turn them out damp-dry. Another development is a dial-selector on a washing-machine, giving different washing treatment to different fabrics.

As for the ironing, there is a choice of ordinary hand-irons, steam-irons or automatic ironing-machines. Hand-irons are available in a wide range of weights, and some take less than a minute to reach top heat. The rotary ironing-machine has foot control, which leaves both hands free to guide the garments through the machine.

Housework these days has the ache taken out of it; vacuum cleaners need fewer attachments and a new toe-touch control turns the swivel head from carpet cleaner into floor brush, saving stooping. They are lighter and more mobile, and brighter colours cheer an inevitable chore.

Automatic dish-washing machines are now within the reach of even the small household, with the introduction of a machine which fits on the draining-board. It twice rinses and power-dries crockery, cutlery and glassware for a family of four or five. A larger model can be bought which loads more easily, from the front, instead of from the top. These machines, big or small, need not detract from that streamlined look in the kitchen, since they can often be teamed with other units to make a continuous working surface or be fitted under a counter.

LOOKING AND LISTENING

When the day's work is—so much sooner—done, records or television are pleasant accompaniments to relaxation. Stereo gives a "large as life" impression; many models are on the market—and those who like doing-it-themselves can buy the component parts of a stereo set to put together at home.

Television sets are not the eyesore they once were. Utilizing the new 110° tube, they are neater and slimmer, yet have greater picture area. Coloured cabinets are available; one firm has a range of four. There are also many portable television sets.

Decca stereogram SG177, 44 gns.; 46 gns. with legs

ELECTRICALLY IN 1960 LIVING ELECTRICALLY IN 1960 LIVING ELECTRICALLY IN 1960 LIVING ELECTRICALLY IN 1960 LIVING EL

● The day will be a busy one for them, but electricity comes to their aid in a big way. It's often not pleasant to get up on a cold, wet morning, but an electrically controlled switch alarm unit helps to make things easier. One unit is a synchronous electric clock, controlling two three-pin plug sockets. Any combination of household appliances can be plugged in, to a total loading of $7\frac{1}{2}$ amps. By setting the indicator hand, it will not only wake you, but make tea and turn on the

Time at a premium for working marrieds

Sunbeam automatic cooker, £11 18s. 6d.

considering PLASTICS

With today's dazzling abundance of plastics to choose from, make sure you know what to buy for the best

AT last plastics are respectable. Once dangerously close to a permanent tag of "cheap and nasty", plastics are now recognized as materials with many advantages and a wide potential. The wonderful world of plastics starts in the home—making it more colourful, quieter and easier to keep clean. It would be difficult to imagine a kitchen without plastics—and no one can dispute their value there. But it is important to look beyond the gay colours and assess the worth of each article from a practical viewpoint.

PLASTICS IN THE KITCHEN

There are two main types of plastics: thermoplastics and thermosetting plastics. Thermoplastics will soften when heated to certain temperatures. This group includes polythene, PVC (polyvinyl chloride), polystyrene, nylon, acrylic and polypropalene. Thermosetting plastics, on the other hand, are soft only during processing, and into this group come melamine, phenolic and urea.

Almost monthly we learn of developments in these plastics. Polypropalene (a well-known trade name for this is Propathene) is one of the newer thermoplastics. It is a plastic more rigid than polythene with greater stain-resistance and slightly increased resistance to abrasion. It will withstand sterilizing in boiling water. It is used domestically for bowls, picnic ware and laundry baskets; for washing-machine agitators and similar component parts. Another good example of improved plastics is *high-density polythene* (high-density Alkathene is a trade description). It has a good rigidity and will stand higher temperatures than polythene, and is suitable for colanders, buckets and hot-water bottles.

Nylon in its solid form is a tough material. It is now used extensively for such things as door catches and ball-bearings which take a great deal of wear. Many refrigerators have a moulded plastic (usually polystyrene) interior. Freed from joins, the refrigerator is easier to clean. There are some exciting new designs in laminated and melamine plastic working surfaces. In the laminated types it is now possible to find matching patterned table-tops and chair seats. A polyester spray finish on kitchen cabinets gives a hard-wearing easy-to-clean surface.

Plastics, of course, have disadvantages. Acknowledge these and reject any item that is unlikely to stand up to its job. Soft, malleable beakers, buckets and colanders are out. Anything that has to hold liquid—or withstand high temperatures—should be rigid. Constant abrasion damages many plastics. Mixing bowls, for instance, can become badly scratched; plastic plates are too easily scratched by steak knives. Hot coals will melt a polythene dustbin, and a cigarette end thrown into a plastic waste-paper basket can start a bad fire.

CARING FOR PLASTICS

Plastics remain easy to clean just so long as the surface stays undamaged. The golden rule is: avoid abrasives. Here's how to take care of plastics.

Laminated plastics and melamine table-tops: Wash with cellulose sponge or cloth, using hot water and mild, soapless detergent. Rinse, dry with a soft cloth. Remove stains by rubbing lightly with soap powder or detergent.

Melamine cups and plates: Rinse immediately after use. Wash in hot water and liquid detergent. Remove stains as above or with bicarbonate of soda.

Interior of the refrigerator: Wipe with a damp cloth. Mop up spills at once. Do not use soap powders or detergents—they may leave a smell.

High-density polythene, polypropalene and polythene kitchen equipment: Rinse first in cold water. Wash regularly in hot water and detergent. Garbage bins and sink-baskets can occasionally be rinsed out with a solution of liquid household bleach.

Plastic trays and storage containers: Wipe over with a damp cloth from time to time to remove the dust.

More pictures and information overleaf ▶

A profusion of colour characterizes plastics. Back: the delightful tray is from a selection at Peter Jones, Sloane Sq., SW 1. Left: lilac Propathene jug forms part of a set (beakers not shown), 14s. 11d., from Derry & Toms, High St, Kensington, W 8. Next to it in lovely pastel tones, two tumblers, from The Tupperware Co., 49 Conduit St, W 1. 12-oz. size, 2s. 9d. each. The red Thermos jug costs £1 3s.; jelly mould, 1s. 3d.; yellow and white scale, £2 2s. 6d. All from Peter Jones. Peeping from the scale pan are salt and pepper shakers. From Tupperware, 5s. 6d. the set. Left front: the Focus de Luxe stainless-steel starter set, with nylon handles, £5 11s., from Liberty, Regent St, W 1. Table, topped in laminated plastic, matches its chair. Table, £13 10s.; chair, £6 19s. 6d., at Peter Jones. Curtaining in the background, 2s. 11d. a yd, from Selfridges, Oxford St, W 1

Barry Warner

GH—9

**Hygena kitchens are superb.
Moffat cookers are superb.
Together they're unsurpassed.**

**HYGENA
MOFFAT**
TWO MINDS BOTH THINKING OF YOU

A bold and bright 1960s kitchen

appliances was actually falling – TV sets, fridges, washing machines and cars all cost less in the 1960s thanks to mass production (although ironically, the mass production which was liberating the housewife made life a misery for the automated production-line worker) and ownership rose accordingly. For instance, by 1971 91 per cent of homes owned a refrigerator, while television ownership went from 75 per cent in 1961 to 91 per cent in 1971. In 1966 4.2 million houses had a telephone compared with 1.5 million in 1951, and by 1970 car ownership reached 12 million (encouraged in the 1960s by the declining railway service).

Swinging in the Sixties

With growing affluence – and the introduction of the Pill – came a new sense of freedom, especially among the 'baby boomers', the product of the post-war rise in the birthrate, and they put the swing into the 1960s, the era of long hair, mini-skirts, free love and Beatlemania.

This feeling of freedom and non-conformity also filtered into the home, where the beginnings of a reaction against mass production could be seen, with individuality taking over from the style uniformity of the 1950s. Terence Conran's Habitat, launched in 1964 selling more individual and ethnic furnishings, was greeted enthusiastically, and the home pages of *Good Housekeeping* show that

Trendy 'essentials' – the rotisserie and the electric carving knife

GO **Moulinex**
GO MODERN

Save time and money with these appliances, designed specially for to-day's housewife

COOK THE MODERN WAY WITH THE   ROTISSOIRE electric Spit Roaster

COMPLETE   13½ gns.

Blue Ribbon Award Winner at
Ideal Home Exhibition,
London 1966

MAJOR MIXER

COMPLETE £8.10s. 7d.

ELECTRIC CARVING KNIFE

£8. 1s. 11d.

GUARANTEED for 12 months
Obtainable from stores and electrical dealers everywhere.

ANDREWS HOUSEWARE MANUFACTURERS LTD.
137 Kirkdale . LONDON S.E. 26

decorating and furnishing styles were becoming more diverse and innovative. Bold-printed fabrics, wallpapers and tiles in bright colours were popular, and open-plan living came into vogue, with a particular penchant for split-level rooms.

In the kitchen, too, colours became brighter and a huge range of wildly coloured and patterned Formica was available. The trend was still for fitted kitchens, and appliances such as cookers, which had by now reached almost every home, became more refined. The hob and oven were separated for the first time, and it became popular to have ovens built in at eye-level. Many homes were converted to cleaner North Sea gas; Sola grills gave balanced, even heat at all settings; self-cleaning ovens with non-stick surfaces were introduced in 1968; and the trendiest home-owners impressed their friends with a rotisserie. The combined front-loading washer/spin drier, previously only found in launderettes, now made its way into the home. In 1962 a sonic dishwasher was developed, which used sound waves, not soap and water, to clean dishes, but this quickly sank without trace.

Small gadgets were still proliferating: almost every household implement now seemed to call for a plug.

Plugs with everything

The new disposable cooking aids merited a guide from **Good Housekeeping**

'**We are replacing the housewife's muscles by electric motors and her brain power by automation.**' **Good Housekeeping**, *1962*

BETTER HOMEMAKING WITH THE GOOD HOUSEKEEPING INSTITUTE

GHI gets off to a good start...

For husbands to give to wives, or vice versa: a mixed bag of bright ideas to help

Might as well get up in computer-style comfort. Attached to this Rima 405 fan heater is Venner's Auto-Point time control. Set the heater switch the night before and the Auto-Point will turn it on automatically when you get up, off when you go to work – and on again in the evening. Neat and efficient with a thermostatic control, the heater should warm your room up comfortably; if you want cool air, just move the switch over to the cold setting. Good portable present. Venner Auto-Point, price £7 2s. 3d.; Rima fan heater, costs about £10 14s. 1d.

Not the sort who likes an alarm claxon for reveille? The Sony Digimatic Clock Radio is an excellent alternative. It can be pre-set to wake you to the chatty tones of Jack de Manio or the sound of a buzzer. Radio can turn itself off automatically. From £30 1s. 6d., in white, red, black or woodgrain

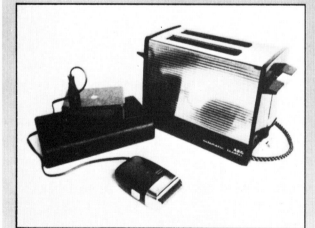

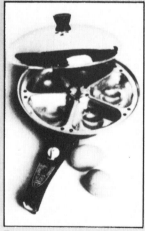

Two gadgets, both ideal for frenetic starts to the day. The Ronson Wayfarer Battery shaver, powered by its own portable battery unit or from the electrical circuit in the car. The pack takes 4 1½-V Ever-Ready batteries. Price, £10 19s. 6d., from most large stores. And if you can't face a fried breakfast, a slice of quickly made toast will at least keep the wolf from the door. Our choice for trouble-free toast – the AEG Automatic Electric toaster. There's a choice of settings to give you any shade of toast you like. The toaster has a chrome and black finish with stainless-steel inside. Price, £7 17s. 6d.

Remembering all the advice about going to work on an egg, we thought this Sunbeam Electric Gourmet Frypan would help you to do just that. It comes with an egg-poaching attachment, so you can have a speedy fry-up or a quick poach. Heat control has settings up to 420° F. Price, £10 14s. 1d.

They say you can tell a man's character from the shine on his shoes, so an early morning shine-up is always a good idea. This Ronson Roto-shine electric shoe polisher saves a great deal of elbow grease. Brush heads and polishing pads are ejected by a push button. Price, £12 12s. 9d.

you wake up, get up, and—more important—get on your way these winter mornings

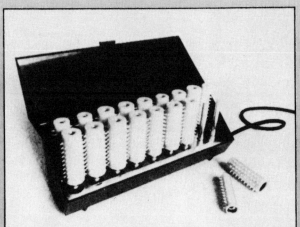

At one time electric toothbrushes were thought to be gimmicks, but now most people realize that they really do clean teeth far more efficiently. Also, many dentists will recommend them for lazy tooth cleaners. We tested the good Halex Electro Dent battery-operated model – £3 17s.

Thank goodness for heated rollers! There's many a married man who must sigh with relief at the thought of not having a wife's head bristling with rollers on the pillow next to his. Newcomers are these smart thermostatically controlled ones by GEC, which heat up in 10 minutes. The set contains 10 large, 6 medium and 2 small rollers, plus clips. Rollers are washable, and extra ones can be bought separately. Presented in a colourful red case, price is £12 9s. 6d. Smaller set costs £9 19s. 6d.

No need to apply make-up in religious semi-dark. This stylish little table spot lamp designed by Harvey Guzzini will throw a good sharp light on things. It's only 11¾ in. high, and mounted on a stable base with felt underneath. The shade swivels in any direction. Orange and other colours, about, £5

For coffee in a hurry, there's a new Vacuum Filter Coffee Maker from Philips. The plastic container fits neatly on top of the electrically heated jug. Put the ground coffee in the container and switch on. The water filters up to infuse with the coffee, then drains down again into the jug where it's kept warm until you want to drink it. To serve, all you do is remove the plastic container and put it on its special drip-stand-cum-lid, £12 5s. 6d.

Girls in flats or families who love boiled eggs should welcome the compact electric egg boiler by AEG, above left. Place one to five eggs in the container, add a measured amount of water to give soft, medium or hard boiling, and switch on. When the pilot light turns off, the eggs are cooked – all very easy. Price, including a special measure, £7 19s. 6d. On to orange juice from a new Moulinex Citrus fruit squeezer. No fiddling with this one – it's an ideal aid, efficient, economical and easy to keep clean. It strains pips and turns on when you press down the orange, £5 12s. 6d.

There were electric toothbrushes, carving knives, shoe polishers, egg-boilers, juicers, shavers and heated trouser presses – many of which were ultimately consigned to the junk room as their owners realised that sometimes it was quicker to use traditional methods.

The Throwaway Society

Sixties developments which really did make life easier for housewives included aluminium foil, cling film, aerosols, and absorbent kitchen towels – all contributing to a more throwaway society. Fortunately, there were new plastic refuse sacks to throw all this rubbish into – they were first used in Hitchin in 1960. Plastics generally became more versatile, while the buzz-words in man-made fabrics were drip-dry and non-iron.

One other advance which no-one today would want to relinquish was the arrival of non-stick cooking. PTFE was invented in 1938, but it wasn't used effectively in cookware until the late 1950s. Early non-stick coatings didn't always live up to their name, and Gill Smedley, who worked in the Good Housekeeping Institute from 1958-1990, recalls worried readers contacting the Institute to ask if it was safe to eat the black bits of coating which were coming off on their food.

With such an array of goods on sale, and with money – and credit cards – to fund it, it's not surprising that shopping became a favourite family pastime in the 1960s, often in the form of a trip in the car to the big concrete shopping centres which were springing up in many cities as part of their regeneration. The decade also saw the rise of the self-service supermarket, made feasible by developments in plastic packaging and freezing which meant that bread, dairy produce and meat could be bought pre-weighed and wrapped in a big weekly shop – and they could be carried home in the new plastic carrier bags. The one-pack meal and boil-in-the-bag food were also 1960s babies. As a result of these changes, the amount of time

Non-iron, drip-dry and boil-in-the-bag were the buzz-words of the '60s

spent preparing food started to decrease, and the variety of food available increased significantly – also influenced by the beginnings of foreign package holidays, which gave people a broader interest in foreign food.

Television continued to strengthen its grip on the home, with the arrival of BBC2 in 1964 and colour TV in 1967, and by the end of the decade it had virtually achieved saturation coverage. When Neil Armstrong set foot on the moon in 1969, he was watched by millions of Britons. Stereo hi-fi systems were the latest thing, and a high priority in the homes of pop-mad teenagers.

As a result of the combined forces of labour-saving appliances, the Pill and general growth in employment, more and more women were going out to work, and this was reflected in *Good Housekeeping* with articles on working and running a home. There was also a backlash against the 1950s image of the ideal

The rotary ironer, a 1960s brainwave that never really caught on

wife and hostess, and family life was tending to become less formal. All in all the 1960s was a feel-good decade, when home life became more comfortable and more individual choices were available. But there was another side: in 1966 Prime Minister Harold Wilson introduced a wage freeze to try to control the spiralling inflation which was starting to make a dent in pay packets. Meanwhile the much lauded high-rise flats were turning into horror stories. There were strong signs that the affluent society wasn't all that had been hoped for.

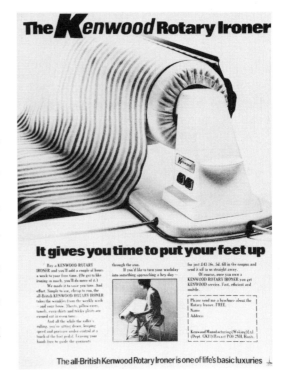

The **Kenwood** Rotary Ironer

It gives you time to put your feet up

The all-British Kenwood Rotary Ironer is one of life's basic luxuries

the 1970s:

FREEZERS AND FEMINISM

HOT ON THE HEELS OF THE OPTIMISM AND prosperity of the 1960s, the early 1970s brought people down to earth with a bang. Politically the decade was dominated by strikes, terrorism, inflation and rising male unemployment. Personal income, which had been growing steadily since 1950, fell for the first time in the mid-1970s. Strikes caused power shortages, and 1973 saw the introduction of the three-day week and power cuts, which highlighted how dependent most homes had become on electrical appliances. For many people, the most dramatic manifestation of the political crisis was that television was forced to stop transmitting at 10.30 p.m. In 1974 both wages and the cost of living spiralled by over 20 per cent; in the same year the price of steel rose by 45 per cent; while the cost of petrol rose from 42p to 72p a gallon as oil prices rose worldwide. During 1978–79's winter of discontent, rubbish piled up in the streets and transport strikes brought shortages of food and petrol.

Green Awakenings

One interesting by-product of the oil crisis and power strikes was a new awareness of fuel conservation, in marked contrast to the rampant consumption encouraged in

I used to be the best dressed waitress in town.

I used to find there was so much running around at dinner parties that I missed out on most of the fun. But that changed when I was given a Sideboard Hostess.

As soon as they're cooked, I pop things like soup, fish and vegetables into the electrically heated dishes and the plates into the heated cabinet underneath. And the thermostat ensures that it's all kept appetisingly hot and in perfect condition for hours.

When my guests arrive I serve directly from it.

Now I've got one I find I'm using it almost every day. With the family drifting in at different times, I do one lot of cooking and know they'll all have a good, hot meal waiting.

Take my advice. Drop a big hint about a Sideboard Hostess. It'll leave you with a lot more time for the really important things—like enjoying your own dinner parties!

Sideboard Hostess £27.23
(excl. VAT) correct at time of going to press

 EKCO

Hostess

ELECTRICALLY HEATED TROLLEYS AND TRAYS

There's a dozen different models — something for **everyone**.

Hostess trolleys promised to make entertaining less time-consuming for women

the stormy seventies

1970   The age of majority was lowered from 21 to 18

Strikes reached the highest level since 1926

LCD (liquid crystal display) was invented

1971   Decimalisation was introduced to the UK

The government ended the supply of free school milk

The first personal computer was made in the US

1972   Britain joined the EEC

Access credit cards were introduced

1973   Purchase tax was replaced by VAT

The first video game, TeleTennis, went on sale

Edward Heath introduced the three-day week; television shut down at 10.30 p.m.

1974   Free family planning on the NHS was introduced

President Nixon resigned over Watergate

The first transmission of Ceefax Teletext on BBC was made

Britain's first McDonald's hamburger restaurant opened

Gillette introduced disposable razors

1975   The radio-operated bleeper was introduced

The Sex Discrimination Act and Equal Pay Act came into force

1976   The first camcorder was developed in Japan

1978   The first test-tube baby was born

The VHS video recorder went on sale in Britain

Bar codes were introduced

1979   The 'winter of discontent'

Margaret Thatcher became Britain's first female prime minister

The Housing Bill gave council tenants the right to buy their homes

the 1960s. When oil prices doubled, the government imposed a 50 mph speed limit and threatened petrol rationing, while everyone was encouraged to save domestic fuel during the miners' strike and power cuts. In 1975 the government launched its 'Save It' campaign, and *Good Housekeeping* helped out with articles on energy saving, looking at issues such as insulation and recycling. Manufacturers began to consider the issue too, in the beginnings of a movement towards environmentally friendly machines which grew in the 1980s.

Despite these political upheavals, the 1970s saw the influx of appliances into the home continue at a steady rate. By the end of the 1970s 92 per cent of homes had a fridge, 79 per cent a washing machine, 97 per cent a television (two-thirds of those were colour). Other appliances were still struggling to make their mark: although *Good Housekeeping* subtitled a 1974 feature on dishwashers 'Not so much a luxury, more a way of life', by the end of the decade only 3 per cent of homes had one, while only 19 per cent had a tumble drier. The microwave had made its debut in only the most progressive of kitchens. Waste disposal units, similarly, seemed like a wonderful idea but were fitted in a small minority of homes: they were noisy, slightly frightening, and anyway, the increased reliance on pre-packed food rendered them less useful. And by 1979 only 55 per cent of homes had central heating.

Technologically, the big story in the 1970s was the silicon chip. The chip was at the heart of computer development, and its real heyday came in the 1980s, but during the 1970s chips made programming on washing machines, dishwashers and tumble driers more sophisticated; they were also used in hi-fi systems and calculators. Other refinements continued: ovens' automatic timing was improved, ceramic hobs were developed for electric cookers, and electric rings now heated up more quickly, removing one of their main drawbacks, with the result that by 1979 41 per cent of homes were cooking with electricity, though gas fought back with its 'cookability' slogan. A new fad was the slow-cooker, which promised to cook your

This tiny particle is the biggest single advance in washing machine history. It is a computer.

SERVIS BRING THE COMPUTER AGE TO WASHING MACHINES.

The Servis Selectronic is the world's first computer controlled washing machine.

By being the first to take step, Servis have achieved a genuine breakthrough: the biggest ever in the history of the washing machine.

The breakthrough gives Selectronic unprecedented reliability, exceptionally simple push-button controls and, at the same time, makes it radically easier to service than any other automatic washing machine.

SPACE AGE RELIABILITY.

Until now, every automatic has been controlled by a mechanical timer with its maze of wires and moving parts. It is in this area that a great many washing machine faults and breakdowns arise.

The Selectronic's computer brain hasn't one moving part, and it has eliminated the need for the 56 others that can be found in the controls of conventional automatics.

In other words, Servis have introduced to washing machines the kind of reliability that put man on the moon.

FIVE-YEAR GUARANTEE

UNIQUE 5-YEAR GUARANTEE ON UNIQUE COMPUTER CONTROL.

We have taken the unprecedented step of giving the Selectronic's computer control unit a 5-year guarantee.

No other washing machine manufacturer promises you such long term peace of mind.

But then, no other washing machine control unit promises such long term reliability.

COMPUTER APART, IT IS STILL A MARVELLOUS MACHINE.

The Selectronic is today's most progressive machine with a host of features to recommend it.

The easy-to-use controls are sensibly childproof.

It has 12 programmes including special features such as Bio Wash, Rinse and Spin, Fast Wash, an independent or combined Pre-Wash and Fabric Conditioning and Rinse Hold facilities.

High speed, 800 rpm spin drying. (Even so, it's amazingly quiet and stable). Plus a full 9lb wash load capacity in a space-saving 22¼" wide by 22¼" deep.

From top to bottom, the Selectronic is better thought out and more convenient to use.

It is the right height for fitting in with most modern kitchen units.

It has a stainless steel drum.

Four rollers for easy mobility. A removable, laminated worktop.

And it has a higher port-hole, to make it easier to load and unload.

EXPENSIVE? YES. THE MOST EXPENSIVE? NO.

The Servis Selectronic is the most advanced washing machine in the world, but it is not the most expensive.

There are machines that cost more and offer less.

All in all, the Selectronic represents excellent value for money.

No conventional automatic has all its computer age benefits.

Here at Servis we are proud that the Selectronic has our name on it.

SERVIS SELECTRONIC

Servis Domestic Appliances Limited. Kings Hill, Wednesbury, West Midlands WS10 7TE.

meal while you were out – but only if you wanted to eat casseroles and stews. Front-loading washing machines became increasingly popular, spin speeds improved and more programmes were introduced to cope with the growing variety of man-made fibres. Cheap, versatile and easily washable, synthetic fabrics were now used for clothes, sheets, soft furnishings and carpets. This was the era of brushed nylon sheets, nylon cellular blankets, shag pile carpets – and a lot of static!

BETTER HOMEMAKING WITH THE GOOD HOUSEKEEPING INSTITUTE

PRACTICAL PLASTICS WITH A TOUCH OF CLASS

Today, there's a new generation of plastics to use around the house. They're no longer cheap and nasty substitutes for other materials, but originals, acceptable in their own right. Colours are clear and cheerful, cleaning and maintenance are minimal, and breakages practically nil, since many plastics just about bounce if you drop them. From the once merely ''disposable'', they've progressed to being near indispensable. Here's the best of a very bright bunch to use around your home

Frozen Assets

The appliance that had the biggest impact in the 1970s was the deep freeze. In 1970 only 4 per cent of homes had one; by 1978 the figure was 41 per cent – and with this went a huge increase in the purchase of pre-packed frozen food and a decrease in the time spent preparing meals. *Good Housekeeping* responded to the boom with

The freezer was the decade's 'must have' appliance

Plastics became ever more refined

regular advice on home freezing. This dependence on the freezer was probably linked to the rising number of working mothers: between 1971 and 1976 a million more married women joined the workforce. As heavy industry declined and electronics and service industries grew, there were more jobs for women, and the feminist movement, kick-started by the publication of Germaine Greer's *The Female Eunuch* in 1970, encouraged women to fight for equal rights and equal pay at work. The Equal Pay Act of 1975 enshrined this in law, and the

Salmon in October.   New Potatoes in November.   Corn in April.

Asparagus in September.   Raspberries in December.   Pheasant in June.

Freeze it when it's plentiful. Eat it when it's scarce.

There's a better way of living with electricity
The Electricity Council England & Wales

Equal Opportunities Commission was set up to make sure that women got a fair

deal in the workplace and elsewhere.

All in all, there was more to
tempt married women to work than

'Not so much a luxury, more a way of life.'

Good Housekeeping *on the dishwasher, 1974.*

ever before – except the failure of most men to recognise any need to change their

domestic role. *Good Housekeeping* was well aware that working outside the home

wasn't necessarily good news for women. A 1974 article on the wife who works

commented:

> 'In nine cases out of ten, she simply adds to her burden by taking on two roles
>
> instead of one. Now, in addition to shopping, cooking, washing, entertaining,
>
> looking after children she must be clear-headed and decisive, with make-up on
>
> and hemline straight at whatever ungodly hour she starts work each day. OK, say
>
> the feminists, make men share the household chores. But, as the saying goes, "It
>
> is man's pride to support his household not to clean it." It's unfair, it's maddening,
>
> but that's the way it is.'

Men might have been reluctant to lend a hand in the kitchen, but they were proving

keen to grasp a power drill. Home ownership (and house prices) rose in the 1970s:

by 1979 over half of families owned their own home, and with this went a new

interest in home improvement and DIY. A survey in the late 1970s showed that 51

per cent of men cited DIY as their main leisure pursuit (after watching television, of

course), and throughout the country a trip to the DIY store became a Saturday

family outing. A host of power tools was available to help men with the agonising

task of constructing flat-pack furniture, while ready-pasted vinyl wallpaper promised

to make paperhanging easier.

Family entertainment still revolved around the television, although

cinema-going went through a small renaissance after the arrival of multi-screen

cinemas in the mid-1970s. The average Briton was watching 16 hours of television a

week in summer, 20 hours in winter; and colour gradually replaced black-and-white

How could you live with a dull lounge like th

From curtains and clothes to bedlinen, man-made fibres invaded the home

ICI fibres transform every room. See these fabulous home fashions at your nearest stockist now.

You can make it bright and beautiful—
it'll cost a lot less than you think!

ess your lounge like you always
yourself. Bright, colourful and
onable — in ICI fibres.
ansform granny-type chairs with
ch covers in 'Bri-Nylon'.
ike the windows glow with elegant
ins in 'Bri-Nylon' or 'Terylene'

and white nets in 'Terylene'.
They look much more expensive
than they really are.
They're easy to wash — and they
dry in minutes. Complete the picture
with a beautiful carpet in ICI Nylon,
'Bri-Nylon' or 'Terylene'.

WE CAN'T ALL BE SUPERWOMEN

The career wife feels guilty she's not at home,
the housewife that she's not at work.
Mary Kenny, author of *Woman x Two*, thinks it's
time we stopped worrying and learned to follow
our own inclinations

WE LIVE at a time of tremendously expanding opportunities for women. Recently, a young teacher in a convent in Sussex asked the girls in her Sixth Form what they wanted to do after leaving school and the *breadth* of their ambitions really astonished her.

"They were all so adventurous. They wanted to be lawyers and surgeons, linguists and kennel maids. One girl wanted to join the Merchant Navy! From the whole group of about fourteen girls only one mentioned marriage, but even for her it was very much in the distant future."

You might of course, get a different range of answers if you went to a South London comprehensive, but I wouldn't mind betting that among any group of Sixth Form girls today you'd find serious ambition.

Twenty years ago, in a very similar convent which my sister attended, sixteen of her form of eighteen went on to do secretarial courses with a view to filling the gap as undemandingly as possible between school and marriage. As Lady Masham, the distinguished peer who does so much work for the handicapped, remembers, "In the Fifties nobody took the career thing for women seriously."

Things *were* different in the 1950s. Only about 22 per cent of married women in Britain had jobs (as opposed to 50 per cent today). Even degrees were soon forgotten. A woman I know who graduated from Oxford in 1956 and married the following year, says "it simply didn't occur to you to go on working. Nobody *did*. After the honeymoon, you came home and started home-making: you were a married lady".

This was, if you like, bourgeois life. Those who did go out to work were either very poor or very ambitious. A successful diplomat once told me that the reason he was so tough was because he'd been brought up the hard way — "We hadn't a brass farthing after my father died and my mother had to go out to work" — and he had obviously felt the loss of face keenly as a child.

Getting married and going on working in those days was called, very disapprovingly, "having your cake and eating it", and the social pressure against it was considerable. No day passed without some newspaper's publishing a reprimand, usually by a bishop, to working wives whose selfishness was deemed the cause of every social evil.

Now, not only have things altered fundamentally, but social pressure has gone to the other extreme and often the stay-at-home wife is made to feel a failure. As one such wife wrote to the *Daily Mail* a few months ago, "I'm forced to pause with guilt before the innumerable forms where I must reveal myself as — *Occupation: Housewife*. Sometimes I rebel and write in 'slave' or 'naturalist' or 'child psychologist' — anything which helps me avoid the blunt truth."

A friend of mine who gave up her job at the Foreign Office soon after getting married, agrees. "One is made to feel so *wet* nowadays if one isn't doing something frightfully high-powered and interesting," she says. And someone else I know who seems happy

except for her obsessive hang-up with her own lack of ambition put it this way: "One is simply *expected* to have a husband, a lover, umpteen adorable children and an amazingly fascinating job—and I feel constantly guilty that I seem to spend most of my time doing nothing in particular."

In fact, whenever women discuss the direction or substance of their lives, the word that most frequently seems to crop up is "guilt". "I'm always meeting women who translate, or teach, or make and sell macramé by the ton," laments a research zoologist who made the decision to stay at home with her child, "and I'm beginning to feel very uncomfortable and guilty."

The truth is that *whatever* women do they feel guilty now. The woman who opts for home feels constantly guilty because she doesn't have a job as well. And career women, although they may be better at hiding it because the tide of fashion is more in their favour, also live with a constant, almost imperceptible residue of guilt at the thought of all the things they are leaving undone.

We're lucky to have the freedom of choice — there are still many women in other parts of the world who haven't — but always there's a strong pull to keep aiming high on all counts and this is where the conflicts arise, between what we feel we "ought" to do and our inclinations. Generally speaking, whereas a man is really only expected to be good at one thing, a woman is meant to be good at three. She doesn't actually have to be a good wife, a good mother and good at a

job — but she does *war*
Helene Hayman, the yo⟩
for Welwyn, confesses
her husband's shoes s⟩
trace of being down-at⟩
pang of guilt assaul⟩
Another working wor⟩
shop manageress, says t⟩
hates sewing, yet if sr⟩
one of her sons going o⟩
a hole in his jeans inste⟩
neatly-sewn patch, she⟩
"It's me. My children a⟩
lected because I'm goin⟩
work." It's the bending
backwards-to-expiat
sense-of-guilt syndrom⟩
The anomaly is, of cours
guilt in itself is not an ⟩
unproductive emotion:
galvanise you into
things; it's a kind of by-p⟩
of a sense of responsibili⟩
woman who gets a pang⟩
she sees children's jea⟩
need mending isn't just ⟩
idle guilt, she's also sr⟩
that she *cares*. And ca⟩
important. Frankly, ⟩
are more altruistic than n⟩
1976 survey in geriatric s⟩
found that the lonelie⟩
people are the childles⟩
people who have had⟩
only. Daughters look aft⟩
old folks, sons don't so r⟩
So the guilt that women⟩
feel is fundamentally p⟩
their nature, and it woul⟩
much harm either, exce⟩
some women finish by ⟩
themselves too hard⟩
something finally breaks⟩
They are, however, mani⟩
by society. There are ⟩
when it suits societ⟩
women to come into the
force (wars, expanding ⟩
omies, the need for s⟩
female skills), and times⟩
it's better to have them at⟩
(post-wars, decline of ⟩

Left and overleaf: As more and more married women worked outside the home, Good Housekeeping *discussed their changing roles*

economic areas), and
sense of duty – for duty,
ilt – which is invoked.
omen allow themselves
o easily influenced and
lated by fashions in
ideas. Every time a
breaks a new barrier of
upremacy it naturally
news, but women at
can be made to feel
inadequate as a result.
s becoming hackneyed
gerate the power of the
it's nevertheless true
any women do feel
sed by the Super-
presented on tv and
here else.
ical stay-at-home wife
m not jealous of some-
e Lady Antonia Fraser
a famous beauty *and*
selling historian *and*
and the mother of six
and madly admired by
sband, etc., but she
y makes me feel a fail-
et you never know: you
never take any apparent
oman at face value. No
er knows the price of
else's achievements,
ieve me, there usually
e.
do have to accept this:
e expansion of oppor-
means the increase of
ions, and thus of pres-
nd stresses. Women
more ambitious now
're also subject to more
More choice inevitably
more regrets, more
ver responsibility, more
nty about decisions,
onfusion about rôles
ons.
e those who take new
in their hands and face
ality – like the young
er thirties with a young

family who felt that the only
way she could get the balance
of her life right was to give up
her job as manager of a uni-
versity bookshop in a very
busy town, because she didn't
like the demands that it en-
tailed. As she explained, "I
can't imagine a job that would
be worth doing to the ex-
clusion of everything else. Obviously, you've got to be com-
mitted to your work, but there
is a limit. I had a family to get
home to, and I think a job
should be amusing."

An employer might feel that
this woman wasn't prepared to
give enough; and, if he disliked
having women around, he
might grumble that the trouble
with married women is that
they do have family re-
sponsibilities. Yet many of
us would agree with this
woman's attitude.

We will never escape guilt
entirely, but we must learn to
cope with it, and the only real
way to do that is to break the
wheel of opinion which blows
us hither and thither, stop
being railroaded and decide
what is right for each one of us.
And that, of course, is one of
the hardest things to do. ☐

*Women × Two, about the conflicts
of home vs work, is published by
Sidgwick & Jackson, £4.95.*

Illustration/Michael Frith

105

A DAY IN THE LIFE
OF A NOT-SO-GOOD HOUSEKEEPER

The perfect wife (1947 vintage) went by the GH book, but when Lesley Garner
(1979) tried the same step-by-step approach, she somehow lost her footing

THERE'S SOMETHING about my housekeeping that brings out the missionary spirit in other people. I have a very smart French friend who descends once a year to take me in hand, and it doesn't matter how much I scrub and dust for days before she arrives, as soon as she walks through the door in a haze of *Jolie Madame* the kettle burns out, the dustbin overflows and all the plugs start overheating. After a week spent dominating my kitchen and telling me how to organise my life, she returns to her own immaculate Parisian apartment infinitely refreshed. And I return, with a sigh of relief, to my natural slovenly ways. Which is perhaps why my mother recently pressed into my hand a well-worn copy of a book which had guided her through the early years of married life, the 1947 edition of *The Book of Good Housekeeping*.

Good Housekeeping readers of thirty years ago obviously needed taking more firmly in hand than they do nowadays because not only does the book give detailed household budgets (rents, rates, taxes, repairs and household renewals – £45 p.a.) but it draws up detailed, minute-by-minute daily housekeeping schedules for idiots. This was where my mother had marked the book firmly. There was even one which exactly matched our circumstances – two adults, baby of one year, small bungalow (well, flat actually) – so, encouraged by the fact that the Good Housekeeping

Institute of thirty years ago was liberated enough to tell its readers to allow plenty of time for personal recreation, stimulation and self-improvement as well as drudgery, I decided to have a bash at following the regime.

Alas, the Good Housekeeping Wife 1947 and I part company at the very beginning of the day. At 6.30am, when she is briskly exhorted to "Rise!" we are all asleep. At 6.45am, as she trips round her house ripping back sheets, flinging open windows, attending to boiler and washing and dressing child, our heads are well under the covers. It isn't until gone 7.30am, when the GH family is well under way, that our daughter wakes and is snuggled into her parents' bed in the fond hope that her mother might snatch another five minutes' sleep. She never does. Instead, kicking us both impartially in the ribs and stomach, our daughter climbs off the bed with excited little cries and rampages happily about the room, opening drawers, kicking over wastepaper baskets, knocking over lamps. At 7.45am, as the GH family chomps self-righteously through its cornflakes, the good parent in our house rises and rescues the baby from the chaos – or is it the other way round? While the primeval forces of child and porridge meet in our kitchen, the good parent washes up last night's dishes and makes tea and toast for the bad parent who is still snuggled up in bed. I'm happy

A DAY IN THE LIFE
OF A NOT-SO-GOOD HOUSEKEEPER

to say that the bad parent, on more than one occasion, has turned out to be me.

At 8.15am, as the GH wife clears away breakfast and washes up, our child is put into its cot or playpen with piles of bricks and books and left to the pleasures of self-education. At 8.45am the GH wife does "Daily washing for child" while we are still reading the morning papers. By 9.15am she is busily "attending to bedrooms, bathroom and lavatory" and rounding the corner towards finishing dining room, lounge and hall at 9.45am. By 9.45am, having made the bed, cleared the breakfast and done a little desultory tidying up, *this* housewife is into her third cup of coffee. She has also changed and dressed child and is wondering if she can get child back to sleep in time to enjoy the coffee undisturbed.

At 10.30am, the GH wife is galloping towards the finishing post on the basic cleaning and is back in the kitchen preparing lunch. What has *her* child been doing all this time? At 10.30am I get out the vac. to tackle the perpetual awfulness of the sitting room carpet. Vac. chokes on invisible broken toy, overheats dangerously and gives off strong smell of burning rubber. Put vac. away again. Make fourth cup of coffee. Hope that GH child is now crawling round its mother's immaculate house dropping Baby Lego, dribbling and rubbing crumbs into her newly swept carpets. My child is wide awake and bored. Decide to take it shopping. Why only one mitten left from each of four pairs? Where are other mittens? In vacuum cleaner perhaps?

At 11.40am that virtuous GH wife gets down to her "Special Work". Special Work? At 12 noon having returned from shops minus the fifth mitten, I suddenly realise child must be fed. Surprised by this every day. What to feed? Run out of special baby food. Give hungry child piece of cheese while I go through fridge. Write "Babyfood" on kitchen notice board. See I wrote "Babyfood" on it yesterday. Feed child scrambled eggs for third day running.

At 12.45pm the GH wife calmly completes dinner preparations for self and child. She's been preparing dinner since 10.30am, for heaven's sake. Obviously not eating scrambled eggs. At 1.30pm she cleans and washes up. Tidies kitchen yet again. Washes and changes – what or whom? Where *has* her child been all morning? Mine now turning sitting room into adventure playground. 2pm: Time for snooze for her. Me too? Resist temptation and nobly clear sitting room floor again. What is needed for toy-strewn floors is not vac. but rake. Why no rakes in Mothercare?

GH housewife is now told to spend afternoon "Attending to child, shopping, mending, gardening, etc." Why did nobody in the 1947 Good Housekeeping Institute realise that she can only do one of those things at a time? At 3pm when my child wakes we repair to the kitchen while I get on with making bread (ah, this is the life), peeling potatoes, etc. Child opens all bottom cupboards. Opens oven. Tries to open washing machine. I give child jug of wooden spoons to bang. Child thinks jolly good. Then child jolly quiet. Find child carefully removing coal from coal bucket. Put coal bucket on top of boiler. Give child book. Child has read it already. Child now gleefully pulling dirty nappies out of bucket and strewing them across the kitchen floor. Put child in play pen. Child disapproves.

At 4.30pm the immaculate GH mother prepares and serves tea for child. Mine gets same at 5pm and we're on the home run towards bedtime. Bath child. Dry and dress and cuddle it. Read Peter Rabbit together. What *has* her child been doing all day? At 5.30pm the GH wife is suddenly told to have "Playtime with child". At 6pm, presumably worn out with half an hour's playing, the GH wife calls it a day and starts putting her child to bed. At 7pm my child gets a last lullaby and falls asleep. At 7pm the GH wife is smugly serving her husband his evening meal. Lucky GH wife now has evening free for "Recreation". So do I. I suspect the only thing we've got in common is that we're both too tired to do much about it. □

Wake up darling, it's a cheerful day...

Mum said we should have stayed with the plain pink walls, but looking through Crown's super new Vinyl range, I saw this paper which *was* pink – but much more fun - it reminded me of peacocks.

So we agreed on that and – c'mon, wake up for heaven's sake – it's Monday morning already!

Crown Vinyl P 85832 and a nice cup of tea that's fast getting cold.

...the coffee's perking in my pretty little kitchen...

You should have seen it before we moved in!

This new Crown range is astonishing. We've somehow turned a squalid little kitchen into a bright new *modern* one. Mother's terribly jealous.

P85846 Vinyl is a bright new wall covering from Crown that resists grease and steam and scuffing - like a dream.

...and the sun is picking out the pattern on the living room wall.

We chose this particular paper in Crown's fabulous range of Relief Decorations.

It's called a Supaglypta – and the thing about it is – it's masked the roughness of the old wall, beautifully.

It's very pretty, very up-to-date and you can paint that lovely raised pattern any colour you wish. We painted it Hot Sahara to warm us all up.

Next year, central heating!

Supaglypta RD 609 with two coats of Crown Emulsion – Hot Sahara from the swinging range of exciting new colours.

Crown, beautiful Crown!

for the new man of property and his woman of taste.

sets. The other major form of home entertainment, hi-fis, were developing into 'music centres', and becoming smaller and more sophisticated thanks to the silicon chip. Early video games, played through the TV screen, were extremely primitive by modern standards but proved instantly popular nonetheless.

At the end of the 1970s video began to make its mark. It became viable for domestic use after the development of the VHS format in 1976, and the first video recorders were sold in Britain in 1978. By 1979 230,000 British homes had one – 80 per cent of them rented, as the early models, and the cassettes to go

The 1970s saw the launch of VHS video

in them, were expensive. In 1979 the first video hire chain of 40 shops was opened, with a recommended hire rate of £5.95 per video – amazingly expensive by today's standards. From this standing start, the video made its way into 60 per cent of homes by the end of the next decade.

the 1980s:

CHIPS WITH EVERYTHING

THE 1980S SAW CONSPICUOUS CONSUMERISM reach its peak. In a decade of Thatcherism, escalating house prices, rising home ownership and small enterprise, and the large-scale privatisation of gas, water and telecommunications all combined to create a booming economy. Borrowing and the use of credit cards also blossomed – and comedian Harry Enfield's 'Loadsamoney' character instantly struck a chord. The image that seemed to sum up the 1980s was the designer-clad Yuppie (Young Urban Professional) who worked in the City, mobile phone clenched to one ear, doing deals while driving a Porsche back to a Docklands flat furnished in matt black and chrome.

The High-Tech Decade

While life wasn't like that for the majority of people, some Yuppie ideals did filter down into the average home. 'High-tech' was a buzz-word for everything from washing machines to camcorders, and science fiction seemed to be turning into science fact as the microchip changed the world. As chips came down in price, so did the products in which they were used – calculators, for instance, which had cost £70 in 1972, could be bought for around £7 in 1982, and were much smaller and

KITCHENS
coping with a mean cuisine

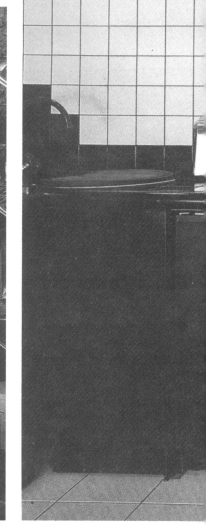

A SIMPLE KITCHEN was what Jennie and David Hillman wanted when they moved into their turn-of-the-century flat five years ago. The rented flat that they left had been decorated with an abundance of florals and chintzes, and they longed for simple, clean lines – particularly as their new basement kitchen was only 9ft square and had little natural light.

They chose a black and white colour scheme accessorised with bright red and stainless steel. Jennie hates wallpaper, so they opted for tiles instead. David did all the work himself, including the tiling. Three walls are tiled white, grouted with grey and relieved by a pattern of black tiles behind the hob and sink, and in contrast the wall housing the oven is tiled black and grouted grey. All the work-surfaces are tiled black, too, and a white ceramic floor completes the graphic look.

They moved the sink from its original position (where the oven is now) to the left-hand corner and installed two

The eighties look
– a high-tech
combination of
black, white and
shining chrome

:ular sinks either side of the corner nake maximum use of the space. The ts aren't used for storage but house all ir Zanussi appliances. They bought ite Zanussi door fronts and sprayed m black to match the colour scheme. rage is provided by industrial wire-sh shelving, which holds essential

cooking equipment – other pots and pans and vegetables are kept in the recesses above and below the oven. David built the square section above the hob to hold the extractor fan, and used the space to fit recessed Erco lights. Other lighting is provided by strategically placed spotlights.

Jennie would love more space for a food processor and other gadgets, but there simply isn't room. She adds, however, that the big advantage of a kitchen with a clearly defined colour scheme is that it makes shopping for kitchen items easy – if it's not black, white, red or stainless steel it's just not bought!

the high-tech eighties

1980   The first Sony Walkman Personal Stereo was developed

1981   Prince Charles and Lady Diana Spencer married

1982   Unemployment hit 3 million for first time since the 1930s

The Falklands War

The first liquid detergent for washing machines was produced

Channel Four was launched

1983   Breakfast television started transmission

The compact disc player was launched, with a choice of 300 CDs

The first cordless phone became available

Apple introduced the computer 'mouse'

1984   The AIDS virus was discovered

Satellite TV was introduced

British Telecom was privatised

1985   Amstrad launched the PCW word processor

The first cellular mobile phone became available in Britain

1986   The 'Big Bang' – deregulation and computerisation of the Stock Exchange – took place

CD-ROM – laser-read compact discs for computers – was developed

House prices soared – London properties rose in value by nearly 27 per cent in one year

Black Monday – stock markets crashed in London and US

1988   All-day opening for pubs was introduced in England and Wales

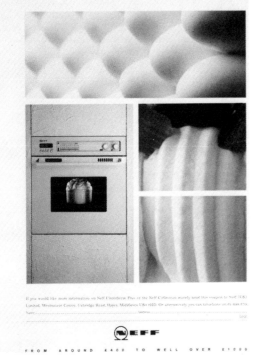

PRACTICALLY ART

If you would like more information on Neff Circotherm Plus or the Neff Collection merely send this coupon to Neff (UK) Limited, Westmount Centre, Uxbridge Road, Hayes, Middlesex UB4 0HD. Or alternatively you can telephone on 01-848-9701.
Name...
Address..

NEFF

FROM AROUND £400 TO WELL OVER £1000

The cooker became a work of art

quicker. As well as helping to bring the price of computers down, microchip technology became standard in the 1980s in programming washing machines and dishwashers, in cookers and microwaves, and in televisions, videos and hi-fis.

The computer age was hitting the home, and this was reflected in how it looked, too. Although there was a lot of individuality in decorating styles, there was a distinct leaning towards black and chrome, with tables and chairs in black ash, black leather sofas, cookers and microwaves in black casings, and metal and grey kitchen surfaces in improved, tougher laminates, with advanced ceramics used for sinks.

The Style Wars

Apart from chip technology, other developments were taking place. Some major appliances such as cookers, vacuums, fridges and washing machines had almost achieved market saturation, and the challenge for manufacturers now wasn't to persuade consumers that they needed, say, a fridge, but that they needed a *new* one. As a result style wars began in earnest – the appearance of appliances had never been so important. Cookers and fridges alike were advertised as works of art; ceramic and glass hobs offered stylish and clean cooking; washing machines and dishwashers vied with one another in the number of different programmes they could offer. Smaller goods such as kettles, toasters and mixers were increasingly made in tough plastics rather than metal, so the range of colours and finishes available increased, and their designs improved too: free-standing jug kettles, toasters which adapted themselves to the size and freshness of bread and sophisticated programmable food processors were more user-friendly than ever before.

towards a
GREENER KITCHEN

THE MARCH OF SCIENCE and technology has done wonderful things for the domestic kitchen. Refrigeration means that food can be stored safely in the home and shopping trips reduced. Automatic washing machines have removed the drudgery from laundry. Tumble driers mean homes are no longer festooned with wet washing. Dishwashers save time and produce cleaner, more hygienic results than hand washing ever could.

The benefits of these appliances are obvious to anyone who can afford them. But it is only now becoming clear that there are problems associated with them which affect the environment. Their use of energy is contributing to the greenhouse effect, which – if not halted soon – will result in the earth's surface becoming ever hotter, so that it will eventually fail to support crops to sustain human life.

Last year, the American grain crop was seriously affected by drought. If the crop fails again this year because of low rainfall, the consequence will be serious and mean further food shortages in some parts of the world.

The greenhouse effect can be halted if we use – and therefore generate – less energy. It is the emissions from the combustion of coal, gas and oil that produce the waste products carbon dioxide, sulphur dioxide and nitrogen oxides that are damaging our planet.

There have been warnings about the problem since the early Seventies, but, by and large, they have fallen on deaf ears. Only now – in the late Eighties – are sufficient numbers of us starting to take the threat seriously.

So what can we do in our own homes, particularly in our kitchens, where we consume so much energy? First, we can be careful when buying new energy-consuming machines. In our *Green Machines* feature (page 8) we test some of the new washing machines and dishwashers specifically designed with 'green' features and give 'green tips' on how to get the best ecological use out of existing machines.

The ground rules for the greening process are simple. When buying any major new appliance, check its energy consumption. If consumers persistently request this information, manufacturers will surely start to provide it as standard. Second, consider whether you really *need* energy-consuming appliances. We're not talking about things like your cooker and washing machine, but about small appliances, which often perform tasks that can be done just as well by hand, even if they do require more elbow grease. Is your electric can opener really a significant improvement on your manual one? Does your electric whisk save significantly more time beating the egg whites than a hand whisk? Our *Green Gadgets* feature (page 38) describes some manual gadgets that work just as well as their powered counterparts.

Meanwhile, there are some do's and don'ts to consider for whatever you're buying for your kitchen. *Don't* buy kitchen units made from wood that comes from the tropical rainforests.

Don't buy aerosols containing CFCs (chlorofluoro-

carbons, which damage the ozone layer). Around 90% of aerosols are CFC free, so check before you buy.

Don't buy batteries that contain mercury and cadmium, which damage the environment when thrown away. Varta batteries are free from both chemicals.

Don't buy plastics containing cadmium for the same reason. Curver Plastics doesn't use cadmium in its household products.

Don't let your kettle get furred up, as it will work less efficiently and use more energy. Make sure you descale it regularly.

Don't use kitchen paper towels more than necessary and, if possible, buy those made from recycled paper, even if they're not as bright white as the brands you usually use.

Don't leave lights on unnecessarily, and consider changing to Wotan fittings, which use 80% less energy than conventional bulbs while producing the same output. They claim to last 8000 hours, compared with a standard bulb's 1000.

Don't boil more water in your kettle than you need. Jug kettles allow you to boil enough for just one cup of tea.

Do try environment-friendly cleaning products. GHI is testing a selection and will report soon on which ones work best. Meanwhile, you might like to send off for *The Whole Thing* mail-order catalogue, which lists over 150 ecologically sound products. Ring 061–236 5116 for a free copy or write to PO Box 100, Altrincham, Cheshire WA14 5SZ.

Do recycle what you can. Find your local council bottle banks and wastepaper collections and use them. Let's hope that councils will take a more active role in recycling and be prepared to collect pre-sorted waste from our homes, as happens in many other European countries.

Do turn on your kitchen hot tap until the water runs hot before turning on the washing machine. That way it won't take cold water from the pipes that needs to be heated up.

Do invest in a seven-day timer to control your central heating and hot water and programme it around your lifestyle.

Do cook sensibly. Don't bake one potato; make sure the oven is full. Microwave cooking is fast and energy efficient.

Finally, *do* think about the way you live.

Put your money where your mouth is on Green Shopping Day on 28 September. Your local paper will have details, or send off for an Action Pack to SustainAbility, 49 Princes Place, London W11 4QA.

Try and catch the Green Homes Exhibition by the Women's Environmental Network, which shows an entire home built and fitted with environment-friendly materials and products. For details, write to WEN, 287 City Road, London EC1V 1LA.   *Cassandra Kent*

Photographs/Ken Kirkwood, Chris Taylor

Good Housekeeping *reflected growing concern for the environment*

Environmental concerns also came to the fore – and cynics might argue that manufacturers jumped on the 'green' bandwagon as one more way to convince consumers to upgrade their machines. Green issues included the depletion of the ozone layer, for which one of the main culprits was believed to be the man-made chemicals chloroflurocarbons, or

By the mid-1980s, 50% of married women worked outside the home, compared to one in five in 1951

CFCs, used as propellants in aerosols and also as coolants in fridges. Recycling, and reducing the use of water and power were also growing concerns, and energy-saving appliances promised to help conserve the world's resources. As interest rates rose and house prices slumped in the late 1980s, and recession set in, many households were more worried about saving their own resources.

Working women were now an established feature of society, and as prices rose their contribution to household finances became more crucial. A mid-1980s survey showed that 50 per cent of married women in Britain worked, compared to 20 per cent in 1951. More of them worked full-time rather than part-time, too, so time-saving at home became more important than ever – as advertisers realised, targeting working women as a distinct group. The dishwasher, which had failed to penetrate homes for so long, finally made more of an impact, from being a feature in only 4 per cent of kitchens in 1982 to 12 per cent by the end of the decade. Once they'd owned one, most women swore they would never return to the washing-up bowl. Fan ovens, which shaved cooking time, grew in popularity too, as did washer/driers, which meant that one machine could be left to tackle the whole washing and drying process – a very long way from the days when washing was a two-day event.

The Three-Minute Meal

But the biggest domestic success story was the microwave, which was used in 47 per cent of homes by the late 1980s. Although it had been invented in 1947, the microwave took three decades to become accepted, partly because of the expense

GH CONSUMER ACTION

TAKING
THE MYSTERY OUT
OF
MICROWAVES

**Although at least 30% of homes now own a microwave, there's still
some mystique – and apprehension – attached to them.
Even today there are people who believe that they could be nuked
if they put one in their kitchen. The Good
Housekeeping Institute dispels some of the myths for you**

IT'S ODD HOW MUCH ALARM microwave cooking has generated over the years. Scare stories in the Seventies didn't help, and there is still widespread ignorance about how microwave cooking actually works.

Yes, rays are produced, but they are not the kind that will slay you if they strike. They are in fact short-wave radiation which is similar to radio waves and *not* the lethal x-rays and gamma rays which build up in the body and do ultimate harm.

There is no evidence that anyone, anywhere, has been injured by a domestic microwave cooker.

HOW THEY WORK
Microwaves in cookers are produced by a device called a magnetron which is housed inside the oven and is, in fact, one of the most expensive components.

The microwaves are attracted by water and will enter food on all its exposed surfaces to a depth of 3cm, causing the molecules to vibrate. With foods which are thicker than 3cm, cooking is done by conductivity; heat produced by the vibrating molecules gradually moves through the food.

PLUS POINTS
● The main advantage of microwave cooking is its **speed**.
● It is also **cheaper to run** and creates **fewer smells and heat** than a conventional cooker.

● It is also **cleaner than conventional cooking** since most foods are cooked covered, and because the heat goes straight into the food, it doesn't burn onto the containers.
● Foods **retain nutrients, texture, shape, colour and flavour** because they are cooked quickly and don't require large quantities of water.
● Microwaving is particularly good for **defrosting and reheating** which can often be carried out in minutes.
● **Ease of use** is also an important factor. Simple-to-use models are suitable for children, elderly people and the disabled.

COOKS' COUNSEL
There has, however, been some concern recently that people can suffer food poisoning when bacteria, such as listeria, are not killed during reheating. Some foods – in particular pre-cooked ready-meals – may not be reheated sufficiently in some microwave ovens. The general view is that listeria is destroyed after being held at 70°C for a minimum of two minutes, but many dishes which are microwaved only briefly may not reach this temperature – or not throughout the whole dish.

The problem lies in the fact that there are around 250 different models of microwave oven currently on the market. They vary in power output and capacity, and even those with the same wattage may cook more or less effi-

ciently if they have a different cavity size.

The Ministry of Agriculture, Fisheries and Food is looking at the problem and hopes to report on it shortly. There is also some food industry-funded research in progress.

We on GH believe that microwave ovens should not be made the scapegoats for the food industry's failure to (a) label foods with sufficient information about cooking so that people with any kind of microwave are able to cook safely, and (b) come clean and tell the public that certain foods are *not* suitable for microwaving.

Meanwhile, we endorse the advice of Jenny Webb, home economist to the Electricity Council who says, 'Turn, stir or rearrange food regularly. Check that it's cooked all the way through. Don't eat something that's obviously not cooked properly even if you have followed the manufacturer's instructions. After all, you wouldn't serve a pan of half-warm soup from a pan on the hob just because you'd followed the manufacturer's instructions on timing.'

FEATURES TO FIDDLE WITH
Sensor cooking
Most sensor cooking works by humidity. A sensing device in the roof lining calculates the required cooking time on the basis of the temperature of steam released from the food.

To ensure this works correctly, food must be cooked covered, either with a

of early models, but also because of suspicion about how it actually worked – it just didn't seem natural to heat food without heating the container around it. But now its time-saving benefits were finally appreciated. *Good Housekeeping* began to feature microwave menus, manufacturers were able to market whole new ranges of microwave ware, and a host of ready meals in microwavable trays came into the supermarkets – the truly lazy could eat them straight from the packet and save on washing up too. Despite the number of

Early home computers and video cameras alike were expensive and cumbersome, but they rapidly shrank in size and price

working women, men were still failing to rush into the kitchen in great numbers – though they did take charge of the barbecuing, which became a favourite summer pastime, with the smell of charred sausages drifting over suburban gardens.

The biggest change outside the kitchen came in the shape of the home computer, which reached 19 per cent of homes by 1989. Initially hailed as a tool for the whole family, on which Mum and Dad could write letters and do their household accounts, the vast majority were actually used for playing games. Early models, such as Commodore's Amiga and the Atari, were expensive, and in many homes the only people

who knew how to use them were under the age of 16 – but the children playing games on their computer in 1989 will be the computer-literate adults of the future.

While children were replacing one screen for another, the television was still the major source of adult entertainment. The launch of Channel Four increased choice, while breakfast TV, launched in 1983, made all-day viewing a possibility. Satellite (and cable in limited areas) brought access to hundreds of channels, and the distinctive dishes became a feature of the British street. The rise in video recorder ownership, meanwhile, was astronomical – by 1989 60 per cent of homes had one, and video rental stores were springing up on every street corner.

Camcorders grew smaller and cheaper, so that more and more people could fascinate their friends with holiday films and shaky recordings of little Johnny's first steps. Hi-fis grew smaller and smaller, with a craze for all-in-one stacked 'midi' systems, and music aficionados raved about the sound quality of the new compact discs, although these, and CD players, were initially prohibitively expensive.

Telephone ownership also rose in the 1980s, from 76 per cent to 87 per cent, encouraged by the end of British Telecom's monopoly, and by a far greater variety, including cordless phones, and coloured and novelty phones.

One feature which became common to televisions, videos and hi-fis in the 1980s was the remote control – and so the couch potato was born. Combined with alarmist reports on the general unhealthiness of modern life, this fostered interest in keeping fit at home, creating a market for celebrity fitness videos and home gym equipment. But for many working women – running a home, looking after children and holding down a full-time job – despite the sophisticated gadgetry at her fingertips, there simply weren't any spare minutes left in the day for leisure.

KITCHEN UNITS BY ELIZABETH ANN

In the 1980s, more and more women played a dual role of housewife/ career woman, as this advert reflects

*H*ow on earth do you do it?

A job. A home. A family to look after.

You do it with a little help where it matters most. In the kitchen. Take the cooker you see here. It's electric.

It knows that all you need is a small oven most of the time. But not all the time.

A double oven for the double life you lead.

It also knows you need a big oven some days. But not every day.

So it has both.

The smaller oven is for smaller meals, the kind you have in the evenings, when you come home from work.

And the big oven is for big meals. Important meals. The kind when you all sit down, all together.

A cooker that knows all about the kind of life you lead. And that's a relief!

COOKELECTRIC

TAKE CONTROL

The Electricity Council, England and Wales

the 1990s:

BACK TO THE FUTURE

AS *GOOD HOUSEKEEPING* CELEBRATES ITS 75th birthday, the standard of living in Britain continues to rise. Despite several years of recession, ownership figures show that the vast majority of homes now have a television, a fridge, washing machine, tumble-drier and telephone; most have a car and central heating. Surprisingly the dishwasher still lags behind, featuring in only 23 per cent of homes, despite the fact that most homes which have one couldn't bear to be without it.

Multi-ownership has also become significant – many homes now have more than one telephone and television, and houses with teenage children may have two videos and hi-fis. In households where both partners work full-time they're likely to have two cars.

The Thinking Machine

The emphasis in the modern kitchen is on 'intelligent' appliances which do the 'thinking' for you. So-called 'fuzzy logic' means that washing machines and dishwashers can monitor the size of the load and modify the amount of water, length of wash and detergent used accordingly – saving money as well as the environment. Tumble driers switch themselves off as soon as the washing is dry.

I think, therefore I am . . .

At Miele, we're constantly thinking of new ways of using advanced technology to make life simpler. That's why all our washing machines are fitted with the unique Novotronic control system that does the thinking for you.

. . . Novotronic

All the programmes you need for excellent wash results are available at the turn of a single switch. Electronic control means fewer moving parts and less wear and tear. Quiet and economical to run, the low water consumption saves electricity and detergent too. And caring for the environment is just one of the many benefits of Novotronic control. Once you've selected a programme, it can't be changed by inquisitive children. It even has built-in diagnosis to cope automatically with low water pressure.

FOUR YEAR
FREE
EXTENDED WARRANTY

PARTS AND LABOUR
WORTH £90*

When you have more important things to concentrate on, Novotronic intelligence can take care of itself. Miele Novotronic washing machines – certainly worth thinking about.

Miele
Anything else is a compromise

For details of your local stockist, please call (01235) 554488

The Free Extended Warranty promotion applies to all new purchases of Miele major domestic appliances made between 1st September and 26th November 1995.
*Combined cost of Miele Double Cover and Double Cover Plus Extended Warranty schemes for Miele washing machines.

HOW MANY
KNOBS DO YOU
REALLY NEED?

How much complicated technology? How many intricate

operating instructions? Wouldn't you like to

spend less time thinking about your wash?

The Indesit 1080 only has one knob.

THE ON/OFF KNOB

That's not to say it's

basic, just simple to use. You

select a programme and the

1080 does the thinking for

you. It sets the temperature,

the length of the wash and

the spin speed. The built-in

ec /sense mechanism weighs

the load and decides the amount of water to use to avoid waste.

The 1080 is available **exclusively at Comet.** So why not drop in,

and you can find out about the "Buy

now pay in 1994*" payment offer.

indesit

WHY PAY MORE?

*Buy now pay in 1994. For example, cash price = £349.99, deposit 20% = £70.00. No further payment for up to 8 months after the purchase date. Balance of £279.99 is payable in full within the 8 calendar month period. Subject to status and cannot be guaranteed. Comet is a licensed credit broker for this service. Comet Group plc, George Street, Hull. Ask for a written credit quotation at your local store. For details of nearest/local Comet store, ring 081 200 0200.

the new-age nineties

1990 Britain's first home shopping television channel was launched

In-car television became available

The first fully biodegradable plastic was developed by ICI

Margaret Thatcher stood down as leader of the Conservative party

1991 The Gulf War

Sunday opening for supermarkets was introduced

The first digital mobile phone was marketed

A newspaper was put on CD-ROM for the first time

Privatisation of UK's electricity supply

1992 The first virtual reality video games were devised

Digital compact cassettes offered an alternative to CDs

1993 The Maastricht Treaty established the European Union

The QVC shopping channel arrived in Britain

The first passenger trains ran through the Channel Tunnel

1994 Interactive television became a reality in the USA

The National Lottery was launched in the UK

Britain's first female vicars were ordained

1996 The Prince and Princess of Wales divorced

1997 *Good Housekeeping* is 75 years old

The new generation of concentrated biological detergents can be used at low temperatures, also saving on bills. Microwave ovens can sense what they're cooking and set time and temperatures accordingly. State-of-the-art cookers have cool-touch doors and electric hobs with heating elements hidden beneath tough ceramic glass: heating is by radiant elements, halogen lamps which 'cook by light' and, most advanced and expensive of all, magnetic induction. The latest freezers are frost-free. And as asthma and allergies become increasingly common among children, vacuum cleaners now have filters to help deal with these problems. Yet, although there is now a huge reliance on high-tech gadgets, there has also been a reaction away from the 'designer' style of the 1980s, with a trend towards a more natural and, ironically, old-fashioned look. Natural wood, or wood-look laminates, quarry-tiled floors and rustic-style pine tables are the most popular kitchen style, and in contrast to the 1950s and 1960s kitchen, in which appliances were proudly displayed as badges of status, the modern preference is to hide them away in cupboards. There has been a backlash against the 'fully fitted' kitchen with a return to freestanding cupboards, dressers and cookers. 'Classic' kitchen appliances are now competing against the plastics monopoly: items like metal Dualit toasters, stainless-steel kettles and chrome-and-

*Classics like
the Aga have
taken on a new
lease of life in
the 1990s*

Her gas-fired Aga is the everyday meeting place. "Once you get to know it, it's a friend for life."

If you'd like to find out more about life with a 3'3" wide jade, red, dark blue, green, brown, cream, black o
white Aga that runs on natural gas, economy 7 electricity, solid fuel, oil or l.p.g. send off this coupon.
Aga, P.O. Box 30, Ketley, Telford, Shropshire TF1 4DD. Tel 0952 641100

Name _____ Address _____
_____ Post code _____ Tel No _____

AGHK91

Distributors throughout the United Kingdom and in Eire, France, Belgium, Netherlands, Switzerland, Sweden, Australia, New Zealand, Canada and United States of Americ

Aga. Part of the Glynwed International plc group of companies.

glass blenders are experiencing a renaissance. And the Aga, the epitome of country-kitchen style which has itself weathered almost 70 years of domestic change, is selling well (boosted by the free advertising given by 'Aga sagas'), as are new range-style gas and electric cookers, which look like an Aga or Rayburn but cost much less and don't provide hot water or central heating.

The same combination of high-tech and traditional values is found in food preparation. The mechanisation of the kitchen has certainly changed the way we cook: the

Pre-cooked foods and the microwave have replaced home cooking for many meals

focus of the modern kitchen is often the microwave and the freezer, a duo which many commentators in the 1980s predicted would spell the end of home cooking and the extinction of culinary skills – in much the same way that the rise of ready-made clothes and soft furnishings earlier in the century brought the demise of sewing skills. Why would anyone bother to bake a cake or create a complex sauce when they could pluck something ready-made from the freezer that would taste just as good – and cook it in five minutes?

Housework as a Hobby

It is certainly true that the average housewife today spends less time than ever before on food preparation – surveys have shown that she cooks 30 per cent fewer meals than she did pre-1939, and that the average time spent preparing a meal is under 30 minutes. And takeaway food of all nationalities, often delivered to the door, is an increasingly popular alternative to cooking. But perhaps *because* cooking is no longer a necessary chore, the 1990s have seen it transformed into a leisure pursuit. This has been the heyday of the TV chef. Delia Smith, Keith Floyd and Gary Rhodes are household names, while cookery programmes such as

Masterchef and *Ready, Steady, Cook* occupy prime-time slots. *Good Housekeeping's* cookery supplements and cookbooks are sell-out successes. It seems that career women (and some men) who spend five days a week transferring plastic trays from freezer to microwave welcome the chance to be creative cooks when they have the time. They're assisted by the fact that bigger and better out-of-town supermarkets and constantly improving food preservation techniques have made coriander, quails' eggs and exotic fruits available nationwide and all year round.

One further ironic 1990s twist is the return of domestic staff. The number of working mothers is continuing to rise, and many are beginning to realise that 'having it all' is impossible without extra help. Having every appliance

> *The 1990s have seen a return to old-fashioned, rustic styles, 'classic' appliances – and domestic staff*

under the sun isn't necessarily enough – the washing machine still has to be loaded, the ironing done, the dishwasher filled and emptied, the floors vacuumed. So, like their grandmothers or great-grandmothers before them, middle-class working women are employing nannies, au pairs, cleaners and gardeners – now in greater numbers than at any time since the 1920s and 1930s. And in an echo of the services available in the 1920s, ironing services are becoming popular, and supermarkets are beginning to look at home delivery. Mail-order shopping is another growth area, and today anything from clothes and bedlinen to furniture, books and cosmetics can be ordered over the phone and delivered to the door.

New Ways of Working

Bringing in domestic help is one solution for busy working women. Another is working from home, which more women and men are turning to as home computers make it feasible. Ownership of home computers has taken off in the 1990s – a 1996 survey showed that Britain was the home computer leader of the world, with double the US level of ownership. Almost one in three households has a computer and, though these are still primarily used by young people, in some

WORKING FROM HOME
THE INSIDER'S GUIDE

Do you long to give up travelling to work and tailor your hours to suit your way of life? ALEXANDRA CAMPBELL describes how new technology can help your dream come true

ALEXANDRA CAMPBELL Freelance writer

When I first started to work from home as a freelance writer, I thought that I already had a home office – with a telephone, answering machine, fax, and an old word processor and printer. Within a week I was screaming with frustration. When I phoned, say 20-30 people in a morning, no one could get back to me because I was monopolising the phone line. The answering machine collapsed under the weight of its new workload, the fax slowly creaked its way to extinction and the word processor, hardly more than a glorified typewriter, took offence at the words it now had to process and turned them all into gibberish, known as 'corruption'.

My carefully-laid plans to have an office at the top of the house proved impractical too. Every time I headed upstairs, Freddie and Rosie, then both 3, had to be physically restrained from following me. The chest of drawers did not do as a filing cabinet, and perching on a dining chair to type gave me punishing back and neckache.

It became imperative to sort the whole thing out. Firstly, I decided to move downstairs into the dining room, within reach of the children, but behind a lockable door. I try not to work when I'm in charge of them, because you can't give proper attention to both at once, but life

sometimes refuses to stay in neat little compartments. call you've been waiting for comes in, running up th flights of stairs with two children clutching at your skir much harder than stepping next door and praying for minutes of peace and quiet.

I was able to buy a decent adjustable chair fa cheaply at a second-hand office suppliers. It doesn't l pretty but then neither does neckache. The filing cab also came second-hand, and our dining table, wh seats 10, had a large enough worksurface to take a p sonal computer, phones, fax, my work, reference bo and plenty of magazines.

Alexandra Campbell now has state-of-the-art phones and a high quality PC

Electronic equipment was much more of a worry proper answering machine is essential, and becaus work long hours on the phone, a telephone with a he set makes all the difference. I've now had three lines in: a fax/computer line, a line for outgoing calls, and normal telephone number. I've begun to wonder, thou if there's such a thing as Compulsive Telephone L Installing Disorder as I can't wait to get my fax and co puter on different lines.

The biggest investment was the personal compu and printer. My brother persuaded me to go the wh hog and I haven't regretted it. His main argument w

---

PLANNING YOUR HOME OFFICE

● **FURNITURE** You'll need an adjustable chair, plus a desk and storage. The PC screen should be straight ahead and the top level with your eyebrows. You need good light, but without glare.

● **PERSONAL COMPUTER** (PC) It's usually worth spending as much as you can afford. Make a list of everything you need to do on it. Will the family use it for games, hobbies, homework? Try out the PC in the store. Make

Financial planner

sure proper back-up is supplied by the company. Is there a helpline, and is it available 24 hours a day or working hours only? How long will you have access to it? Can the PC be upgraded? – new programs are released every day.

Ergonomic approach

● **FAXES** Multimedia PCs sometimes include a fax/modem so you can send and receive faxes without having to use a separate machine. Small

machines are fine unless you want to send receive faxes on A3-size paper, or you can choos a fax/phone/answerphone which allows caller to leave a voice message or send a fax.

● **ANSWERPHONES** If you travel regularly, loo for an answerphone with a remote control allow you to retrieve messages via any tone dialling phone. Tone-dialling or touch-tone phone are connected to an electronic exchange and giv access to a number of services. A touch-tone phone beeps when you press the numbers.

URSULA MASON Designer

...t the children would be disadvantaged without access ...alking encyclopedias and educational games. He said ... best bet was a multimedia PC because the services ... expanding so quickly. And I must have a modem, he ...sted, so my articles could be transmitted directly into ... systems of magazines and newspapers. It also ...ans I can use on-line services such as Compuserve ...ich gives access to the Internet), send E-mail, and fax ...ectly from my PC without printing out, which is bliss.

...Of course, proper equipment doesn't eliminate all the ...blems of working from home. The twins are inclined to ...ze the phone, and once the police chased a burglar ... my garden while I was interviewing someone. My ...l piece of advice is: if the telephone rings when you're ...ning the bath, turn off the taps before answering. ...herwise, your conversation will be punctuated by the ...hwater pouring through the ceiling over the printer. I ...ow, I've been there.

Ursula Mason and Paul need a home office each to run their separate businesses

...sula Mason had worked from home before, so when ... set up her company Courtyard Designs (01886-...4640), selling traditionally designed outhouses, sum-...rhouses and garages, she had a good idea of what ... needed. Her husband Paul, who's in the travel busi-...ss, sometimes works at home – a converted hop kiln in ...tshire – so they needed two offices, on a different floor ...m where they live with their two small children. 'We ...th work on the phone a lot, so we didn't want to share a ...m. We didn't realise how much storage space I would ...ed, so I use an extra cupboard, reached by walking ...ough Paul's office, which is irritating for us both.'

...Ursula's contact with customers is entirely by post and ...ephone. There's no 'shop' and manufacturing is either ...-site or at a production plant 15 miles away. 'We build ...ages and summerhouses with traditional methods ...d materials, particularly suitable for period buildings ...ere a modern garage would be an eyesore. The aver-...e order is £25,000, so we're not processing big vol-...es, but we have about six different brochures to send ...t, and I estimate I get around 50 telephone calls a day. ...The main problem I haven't resolved is the telephone – ...nly have one line. I knew when I started that I would ...nt to "grow" the company so I could afford secretarial ...p, but my assistant only works four hours a day, and

there's no point in having lots of phones ringing if there's only me to answer them. I had the call-waiting service for a bit, but it was chaos – I was always breaking off one conversation to answer the other line, and I think that's quite rude. I was upsetting both callers. Obviously I have an answering machine – vital for people wanting brochures out of hours. And a fax, which is also constantly used – but I think I must be losing business through people continually finding me engaged on the phone.

'It's about time I bought a new PC too, as I've had the same one for years. I use it for keeping a database of customers, sending out standard letters, invoices and orders, and doing the accounts. Paul used to run a computer company, so he advises me, and I upgrade the accounts package every 18 months – that always makes a difference. My favourite piece of equipment is a wonderful label printer I can use directly from the PC – essential for mailshots.

'My secretary has a really good £300 chair, which I use if I'm at the PC, and I've got a really big old-fashioned wooden partner's desk which I love. But we've installed a massive wall-to-wall bench-style worktop channelled for wiring for Paul, who has the full multimedia set-up.'

Karen Young's office has to have room for display as well as containing her PC, phone and fax

When Karen Young went to a wedding nine years ago, another guest was about to go on a cake-decorating course. 'I liked the sound of it, so off I went. I soon started doing cakes for friends.' It turned into a business quite quickly, and now Final Touch (0171-371 7646) specialises in wedding cakes and icing cakes with corporate logos.

'It's not very office-based,' says Karen, 'but I needed to convert a room and put in a phone line, fax line and a PC. I use the PC for accounts and sending out letters and invoices. I need to display about five dummy wedding cakes in the office, too, as people come to visit me there, and I have a portfolio of past work.'

Karen and David's two children, Harriet, 15 months, and Emily, 3½, aren't yet old enough to use the PC. 'Their main ambition at the moment is to take everything out of my desk!' Karen doesn't use her PC every day, but she would like one that's smaller, so she could display another cake. 'I could buy a laptop, but the children will be into homework in a few years, so I might buy a multimedia PC for them to use too.'

KAREN YOUNG Cake decorator

Good Housekeeping *keeps its readers up to date with technological developments such as the home office and the Internet (overleaf)*

GOOD HOUSEKEEPING AND *COMET* HELP YOU MAKE THE RIGHT CHOICE

WHO NEEDS THE INTERNET?

Imagine being able to send messages halfway round the world instantly – for the price of a local phone call. Picture being able to browse around a virtual shopping mall – shoes to the left, handbags to the right, then simply press a button to send your order. Or, you have a report to write and need information – your computer gives you access to the latest facts and figures anywhere. This is what the Internet is – a global network of computers linked by phone line and satellite, providing undreamt of possibilities for consumers, business people, academics and the plain nosy. Over one million people in the UK are now wired to the Net and more are signing on every day.

What do I need?

● A computer.
● A modem to link your computer up to the Net via your phone line.
● An account with an Internet Service Provider (ISP) that runs the big computers that enable customers to use the Net. Costs vary from £25 a year to over £100.
● Software to access different 'sites' on the Net. This often comes included in the fee you pay to your ISP. Windows 95 computer operating system will come bundled with its own Net software that will get you on-line.
● Node – the name you call yourself on the Net.

MODEMS come in many shapes and sizes, and prices hover at around £150. Some of the more sophisticated multimedia systems come equipped with built-in modem and fax. If you are buying a modem get the fastest you can afford – slow ones take ages to download information, and you are paying for every second of time. Look for what's called a 14,400 modem (28,800 is even better but more expensive) and for reliability check it is BT-approved.

INTERNET SERVICE PROVIDERS range from the huge – such as Demon and Compuserve – to the small services that simply route your E-mail, messages you can send from one PC to another all over the world. If you want full access to the Net, expect to pay around £100 a year – more if the company charges by the minute for some services as Compuserve does. E-mail-only services are cheaper – they may even be free.

SOFTWARE comes in many forms. Some computers come with their own Net software, which is all you need to get on-line, apart from an ISP. Packages vary but they should offer you E-mail, news support (which gets you into a sort of global bulletinboard, parts of which you then subscribe to according to your interests) and something called file transfer (FTP), which allows you to start pulling software off the Net. Some of this software is free (Freeware), and some, called Shareware, has to be paid for after an 'approval' period. The software may be a game or educational package or communications package, and quality varies. Most is heavily Americanised. Some Shareware or Freeware may carry viruses too.

SHOPPING ON THE INTERNET

Just how easy is it to do some virtual shopping on the Internet? Well, from a brief browse around something called BarclaySquare, a sort of electronic shopping mall, it's certainly possible, but a bit slow, and I'm not sure I couldn't have done it all quicker with a phone and catalogue in front of me, says GH Features Editor Hilary Robinson. But it wouldn't have been as much fun.

HOW DID I START? Well, I cheated. A computer-literate colleague was there to help me. 'Where are we going then?' he asked as we looked at a screen full of little pictures all meaning something to him but not much to me. 'Um, Barclay something,' I said, trying to remember what this new Internet shopping mall service was called. 'I'll try Barclay then,' he said, clicking on a picture then tapping in the letters. About 30 seconds later, up popped a directory of Barclay services in the middle of the screen – banking, travel, business and something called *BarclaySquare*. 'Try that,' I suggested. Just then a sort of

Armchair shopping for wine with *BarclaySquare*

coloured pavement of brand names appeared on screen. I clicked on the slab called Sainsbury's wine. More waiting, then, eureka – a list of wines appears with prices. To make my selection I simply click on my favourite bottles (you buy by the case), then more clicks on the screen takes you to the ordering part. I don't like the sound of the 14-day delivery period or the £3.95 charge, nor the warning that giving my credit-card number puts me from a secured area into an unsecured area. With horror stories of computer crime still fresh, I bottled out.

I decide to have a 'browse' (Netties say 'surf') through the Eurostar area of BarclaySquare. Perhaps I want a trip to Paris instead of a computer game. I spot a bargain Apex fare, London/Paris weekend return at £84. I'm just about to check my diary for possible dates when – crash... Down goes the computer, no doubt overloaded with hoards of virtual shoppers like me clogging the lines. I pick up the phone book to look up Eurostar. Old technology still has its uses.

cases they are being exploited for teleworking. As communication networks improve, and telephone modems enable homes to link up with offices, home working is becoming a reality for more and more people, and for women it can also give a more flexible way of work, helping with childcare and saving travel time. Goods for the home office – computers, modems, faxes and answering machines – are now big business. E-mail and the Internet haven't yet made a big impact on the home, but they seem likely to do so in the future. And home use of the mobile phone and the pager, although still relatively rare, is growing as prices drop.

The computer hasn't replaced the television as a leisure pursuit: television is still the prime source of home entertainment, with some reports putting average adult viewing at 26 hours a week. Ninety-nine per cent of homes now have a set, and almost three-quarters have a video recorder. TV sets are tending to grow bigger, as both sound and vision technology improve, while hi-fis are getting smaller. CDs are now overtaking vinyl, and many modern hi-fis don't have a turntable at all, making entire record collections obsolete.

As Britain moves towards the millennium, it's easy to say that the housewife today has it made – what would her grandmother have thought of washing the dishes with the flick of a switch, or doing the weekly laundry without breaking into a sweat? But it could also be argued that today's working women have been relieved of domestic drudgery only to exchange it for hard work of another kind.

WHAT IS A

The women pictured on the right are both housewives. Yet their lives are totally different. One stays at home to look after her three children, while the other runs a successful home-based business – which raises the question, 'Is "housewife" the right word?' We opened the debate last October with Penny Vincenzi's article, *'What Do You Do?' 'I'm Just A Housewife'*, and the controversy continues.

Most people think they know what 'housewife' means. The marketing men say crisply it's whoever is in charge of the shopping, cooking and cleaning, which means there are 20 million in the UK. So far so good, except that by this definition, 5 million 'housewives' are actually men. Another anomaly: most women with paid jobs, even if they no longer do *all* the household chores, still find that all domestic roads lead back to them. Does this make the female bank manager or teacher a housewife too?

The more you try to define 'housewife', the more the meaning slips away. So is it time to ditch the term altogether? After all, the 15 million women in charge of the cooking and cleaning are also likely to be raising the next generation or caring for a parent, involved in community projects, taking evening classes, and passionately interested in anything from gardening to marathon running. And, thanks to the miracles of technology, you're as likely to find a woman wielding a word processor at the kitchen table as a whisk. Does 'housewife' really cover all this? And if not, what is the right word to describe the rich variety of women's lives? We asked a selection of women and men in the know to give us their views – then we'd like to hear yours too . . .

ANGELA RUMBOLD, 59, Home Office Minister. Married to John Rumbold; three grown-up children, Philip, Polly and Matthew

'I don't know that the housewife exists any more. The old concept of someone who washed on Monday, ironed on Tuesday . . . all that's been gone a long time. But most women still have a layer of domestic responsibility. They feel that if they don't do it, it's almost certainly not going to get done.

'I had a period when I looked after the children and ran the house full time, but I *still* run it. If I walked out, the family would run out of food and clean clothes, and the dog would die. But I wouldn't call myself a housewife – just the person who has to think about what needs to be done.'

SUE LIMB, 45, writer, married to an organic farmer; one child, Betsy, 7

'A housewife does all the jobs that, 100 years ago, women – middle-class women, at least – paid other people to do. That means the work of a cook, parlour maid, upstairs maid, scullery maid, nanny, governess and dairy maid. In many ways, a woman is more weighed down these days.'

CLAIRE RAYNER, 61, agony aunt, author, broadcaster. Married to Des; three grown-up children, Adam, Jay and Amanda

'The cosy, middle-class idea of women sitting at home gossiping has been gone for ages, and women who stay at home full-time are very much in the minority. Now the stereotype is of a woman with a paid job outside the home who still does too much cleaning because men are so bloody lazy.

'I gave up nursing to look after my first baby, but I had to do something with the time, so I started writing. There are aspects of domestic life that I like, tidiness and order, but Des and I have always shared it.'

GILES LURY, 31, account director for Oxo at J Walter Thompson. Married to Karen, who stays at home to look after Rebecca, 4, and Jack, 2

'I think it's a hugely undervalued role in society. You can't really put a value on it at all, because the job is also about being the lynchpin of the family, with all the moral and social roles that implies.

'Is it an enjoyable job? According to the research we did for the Oxo campaign, it seems to be a role of grief and relief. If you ask a woman about family life, she'll talk about getting the children up in the morning, Fiona brushing her hair, making sure Johnny brushes his teeth, cooking a meal which nobody eats . . . and then they draw breath, and say, "Oh, and the little one brought home a picture of me outside the house . . .". That's one of the things that make it all worthwhile.'

LYNNE FAULDS WOOD, presenter of BBC TV's *Watchdog* consumer programme. Married to fellow broadcaster John Stapleton; one son, Nicholas, 4

'The trouble with the word housewife is that it implies it can't be a man's job. My husband uses the vacuum cleaner far more than I do – and constantly tells me so. He tidies and washes up and

HOUSEWIFE?

In 1992, **Good Housekeeping** *celebrated its 70th birthday by asking celebrities to define the role of the housewife*

JENI BARNETT, 42, contributor to LWT's *Six O'Clock Live.* **Married; one daughter, 5**

'A housewife sorts out the whites for the wash, adds the whitener and the fabric conditioner. A non-housewife bundles everything in together and shrugs when it all comes out grey.

'Housewives will always be with us. As long as women give birth, they'll want to nest. Men are wired differently – it isn't important to them that the books are tidy, the beds are made. But the traditional housewife is becoming an endangered species. It's a generation thing – my mother ironed my father's underpants. Our generation is better at realising what's important.'

JENNI MURRAY, 42, presenter of Radio 4's *Woman's Hour.* **Married to David; two sons, Edward, 9 and Charlie, 4**

'I prefer housekeeper or homemaker. We all have homes that need cleaning, but housewife is so specific, as if it's only the woman's job. It's an undervalued profession, even when a man takes it on, as my husband has. What we call him is a continual problem – domestic engineer? I get cross when people ask me how I manage my job, home and family – we're not going to make any progress until people ask men the same question. Have I ever been a housewife? Yes, for two weeks between jobs. I nearly went demented. I'm afraid if I stayed at home we'd live like slobs!'

e Nicholas right down the middle, and
t of my male friends feel the same.
ut I do think the job of housewife has
ged. People care less about cleaning
polishing and more about having a
l time with their children. When Paula
s said that mothers should stay at
e, I think she was basing her opinion
a fallacy. Nicholas is surrounded by
dparents, a very, nice girl who helps us
him, and other people who love him.
a mix-and-match life and I think that's
cal of the life women lead today.'

**TH FLOYD, 48,
k, writer,
adcaster and
ican. Married to
unagh; two
dren from
vious marriages**

ere are women
o are still house-
es – my mother is
t definitely one – but the fact that so
y women now work has changed
gs dramatically. I've met many women
've rarely cooked a meal and who use
nies, cleaners, laundry services. But
re I live in Devon, things still follow
e traditional lines, women running the
e and men going out to work. How-
r, I wouldn't call Shaunagh a housewife.
lead such a strange life, there's no time
either of us to take on traditional roles,
we just muck in.'

HARRIET HARMAN, 41, Labour MP. Married to Jack Dromey; three children, aged 9, 7 and 5

'The word housewife really means that you're bringing up the next generation, usu-
ally with very little reward. You can do it brilliantly and everyone will still take it very much for granted. The housewife is prob-
ably looking after the elderly mother as well as the children. It's a shame that housewives feel oppressed by women who work outside the home, but working women also feel threatened by housewives. But I think the definitions are getting blurred. There are now women working flexible hours from home, and the big dis-
tinction between working full time and not at all is changing, thank goodness.'

VIRGINIA IRONSIDE, 48, agony aunt and author. Lives with her partner; one son, William, 18

'Even people who work are housewives – they're the ones who come home and say "We're out of washing powder," and although the man may be willing to be ordered about, the organisation of the home generally falls to the woman. But it's a role that women don't necessarily want to give up. If my partner organised supper and light bulbs, I'd feel redundant.'

LOYD GROSSMAN, 41, writer and broadcaster, married to Debbie; one daughter, Florence, 3

'There are still women who choose to make running the household a full-time occu-
pation. And when you consider that your house is the most important thing you can own, and the centre of the family, the idea that the job of looking after it should be devalued is crazy. But it's unpaid work, and that raises the question of whether a job has to be salaried to be valuable.'

*What's your definition of 'housewife'? Or can you suggest a better descrip-
tion? Write to GH (Housewife), 72 Broadwick Street, W1V 2BP.*

139

conclusion

NOW THAT WE HAVE MACHINES TO WASH our dishes, clean our clothes, mix our food and suck the dirt off the floor, plus easy-clean surfaces, non-stick cookware and heat and hot water at the push of a button, life in the home is undoubtedly more comfortable and involves less hard work than it did 75 years ago. But sadly, the hours of leisure and pleasure promised since 1922 have failed to materialise.

The modern housewife hasn't really been liberated from domestic work – partly because standards of cleanliness and efficiency are higher than ever before. Washing machines and tumble-driers have certainly made washing easier – but as a side-effect we now change our clothes far more often than our grandparents did. We no longer spend our time starching and blueing, but all those clean clothes still need to be ironed. Modern homes with their light furnishings, pale carpets and gleaming white kitchens show the dirt far more than the heavy draperies and dark surfaces of the early twentieth century, which hid a multitude of sins. The dishwasher saves washing-up time, but it doesn't load itself. Freezers, microwaves, blenders and mixers make food preparation easier, but at the same time standards of cuisine are in many cases more demanding than those of the 1920s, and eating surveys show that there is a trend for modern families to eat different meals at different times – burgers for the kids and a grown-up meal later for mum and dad – which creates yet more work. Add to that the time taken to get to out-of-town supermarkets; and the inevitable school run because no-one wants to let their child walk too far to school these days, and it's not hard to see why women today don't feel as if they have oceans of time on their hands. And on top of that, the majority of married women now also have full- or part-time jobs outside the home.

Time spent on housework has fallen: a 1993 survey showed that the average housewife not working outside the home spent 38 hours a week on housework, while working women spent 25 hours (why are we not surprised to learn that male partners of working women clocked in with a poor 13 hours a week?). This compares well with the 55 hours of 1951 – but it's still a large chunk of time.

If technology hasn't liberated women in the way it promised, it has certainly ironed out the differences in women's lives. The typical homes of working-class and middle-class women were poles apart at the beginning of the century, but today, with near saturation ownership of major appliances, women's daily lives have become more homogenous. Apart from those wealthy enough to have domestic staff, women, be they wives of steelworkers or stockbrokers, miners or MPs, perform fundamentally the same household tasks, shop at the same big-name supermarkets, drive their children to school and switch on the TV to relax in the evenings.

The Future of Housework

When *Good Housekeeping* celebrates its 100th birthday in 2022, will housework be less of a chore? Predictions are that in the next century far less time will be spent on food preparation, and that eating out, takeaways and instant microwave meals will take the place of a home-cooked family meal. This is already happening in America, where houses are being built with smaller kitchens as a result – and where America leads, we often follow.

An alternative American trend which might cross the Atlantic is 'downshifting'. It stems from a feeling that working mothers are trapped in a cycle: they work full-time in order to provide enough money for the second car, the childcare, the convenience foods and labour-saving appliances which they need to enable them to work full-time... The answer for some is to take a step back: to cut down on consumer durables, cars and instant meals in favour of a simpler – and cheaper – lifestyle where one parent can stay at home with the children.

A more high-tech – and perhaps more realistic – vision of the future is on display in a 'House of the Future' which has been built near Brussels, incorporating state-of-the-art developments which not long ago belonged in the realm of science-fiction. It's a home perfect for couch potatoes: everything, from opening and closing windows to adjusting the heating and selecting a video can be done simply by touching a remote control. The television screen is the key contact with the outside world, used to order shopping, for home banking and a range of other services. Kitchen gadgets include an electromagnetic hob that can boil a pan of water in less than a minute and a screen on which you can watch TV while you work, but which also displays recipes and a constantly updating shopping list. Kitchen stock control is operated by bar codes – scan empty packets before you throw them in the recycling bin and they're automatically added to the shopping list (which can then be sent downline to your supermarket for home delivery!).

Other home comforts of the future include centrally controlled heating, lighting, temperature, humidity and curtain opening, and even a computerised gardener, which monitors soil moisture and waters the garden when necessary. With this computer-controlled home, the busy working woman could programme her home from the office, making sure the lights were on, the curtains drawn and dinner cooking in the oven by the time she arrived home. The main drawback is that this house cost £6 million to build – but technology is developing so fast that it could soon be an affordable reality. Whether people want mechanisation to go this far is another matter. Some studies have already shown that there is a resistance to 'fuzzy logic' and that, while people are happy to let a machine do their dirty work, they'd actually rather do the thinking themselves. Whatever the form the home of the future might take, there is every likelihood that in another 75 years' time, the microwave and dishwasher will seem as antiquated as the cast-iron range and gas mantles of the 1920s do to us now.

index